MW00607463

Beautiful LIES

No Longer Will I Hide...

Tameeka N. Robertson

Hadassah's Crown
Publishing, LLC
HadassahsCrownPublishing.com

Tameeka N. Robertson

Published by Hadassah's Crown Publishing, LLC
Simpsonville, SC 29681

Library of Congress Control Number: 2019915649

ISBN 978-1-950894-10-9

Printed in the United States of America

Dedication

This book is dedicated to everyone who has ever been hurt, whether mentally, emotionally, physically or sexually, and to anyone who was told that they were less than or ugly! I hope you find Healing within your Healing!!!

P.S. You are imperfectly perfect just the way you are! Hold your head up high, adjust your crown and walk on with your bad self!!!

Tameeka N. Robertson

Chapters of My Life

Tameeka N. Robertson

Daddy, Are You Coming Back?

Hi there. My name is Makayla. I am six years old. I thought that today was going to be a pretty nice day. Mommy had gotten up and combed my hair in some cute little ponytails. She dressed me in my matching yellow, pink and white short set. After we ate breakfast and Mommy finished my hair, I grabbed my baby dolls and went downstairs to play. I loved my dolls. I always gathered them up and sat in front of the TV downstairs to play with them. Today was no different.

As I sat downstairs watching cartoons, I talked to my dolls during the commercials. Their names were Kerry, Katie and Maria. They were my favorite out of all of my toys. I was in the middle of changing their clothes when I heard Mommy yelling at Daddy.

"Shut up, Gary! I'm so sick of you and all of your lies! Get out of my house!"

"Whatever Olivia. I pay the bills in this house. I'm not going anywhere! You can get mad all you want, but I'm not going anywhere!"

"You don't pay anything in this house, so you can get out and get out now!"

I heard the door slam really loud, which frightened me. I had heard Mommy and Daddy fuss many times before, but they seemed to be okay after they yelled at each other. It made me sad when they hollered. I didn't like it, neither did my sister and brother.

You see, I loved both of my parents but I was a Daddy's girl. I can remember playing with Daddy and him tossing me up in the air. He gave me piggy back rides or put me on his shoulders. We always had so much fun.

There was this one time when he, my sister and I were walking and these big dogs came out of nowhere. My dad picked both of us up and sat us up on his shoulders while he fought off those dogs. On that day, he became My Hero.

Daddy was tall and very strong. He had a lot of muscles everywhere. Even though he had a very deep voice, he was super sweet to my sister, brother and me. Mommy was a lot smaller than Daddy, but you couldn't tell her that. A lot of people liked both of them, so I didn't understand why they yelled so much. I just hated when Mommy and Daddy didn't like each other.

I heard them shouting behind the closed door. I wanted to check and make sure that they were okay, but they always told me that I was a child and to stay in a child's place. I didn't want them to hit or hurt each other. I loved both of them and just wanted the yelling to stop.

I got up and walked over to the bottom of the stairs to see if I could hear what they were saying. I couldn't understand what they were saying, but I sure knew they were super mad. The next thing I knew, the door swung open and I heard them talking again. I ran back over to sit in front of the TV to make it look like I wasn't listening.

"I'm so sick of this back and forth with you, Olivia! You don't want to believe me? Fine! You want me to leave? Fine, I'm out of here!"

"Do you really think that I care, Gary? GET OUT! Your kids and I will be just fine!"

Now, I didn't know why they were yelling or where Daddy was going, but it didn't sound too good. I don't know what she meant about "we will be just fine," but I wondered if something was wrong with her or my sister and brother. Geesh, I hoped that no one was sick. It's no fun being sick. Mommy always made you feel better when you were, though. She made soup, gave you yummy medicine and rocked you to sleep in her lap. I wondered what was wrong!

Daddy came storming down the stairs. He looked so upset. I got up and went over to him.

"Daddy, Daddy! Are you okay? Who is sick?"

"What are you talking about baby girl?"

"Daddy, I heard Mommy say that we will be alright. Are we okay, Daddy? I don't like being sick."

"Yes, y'all are okay Makayla. I'm going to have to leave for a little while but I will be back when I can, okay?"

"Can I go with you please, Daddy?"

"No, not this time Makayla. I will see you when I get back okay?"

"Please Daddy? Can I just go with you for a little while? I will be good!"

"Makayla, I said 'No!'"

I could tell that Daddy was serious but I didn't know why. Sometimes if I begged to go with him, he would tell me to come on. That wasn't happening this day. He was really upset.

Mommy was downstairs and heard me asking if I could go with him.

"Makayla, go sit down. Your dad is leaving!"

"But Mommy!"

"Don't but me child! Go sit down!"

Although I wanted to listen to Mommy so that I wouldn't make her mad also, I didn't want Daddy to go without me. Mommy and Daddy exchanged a few more words. Some of them were really bad words. Next thing I knew, Daddy was walking out of the door.

I knew that I shouldn't have, but as soon as Mommy turned

around, I ran out of the door after Daddy. I ran up the hill to catch him.

"Daddy! Daddy! Wait for me!"

"Makayla, what are you doing? Get back in the house! Now!"

"Daddy, please don't go!"

"Makayla!"

I knew that I would probably get in trouble for not listening to my parents, but I didn't want my Daddy to leave. I also didn't want him and Mommy to stay mad at each other.

I finally made it up the hill and was standing in front of Daddy. I grabbed him by his leg. He couldn't leave us if I held on to him. I sat criss cross on top of his foot and wrapped my arms around his leg as tightly as I could. Maybe he would walk back down the hill to the house with me on his leg, like he normally did us.

"Daddy, please don't go! Please don't leave!"

"Makayla, baby! I have to leave. I'm not sure when I will be back, but I will be back to see you! Please let go of my leg and go back into the house."

By this time, I was crying. I didn't like to see my parents upset like that.

"Daddy, can you take me back inside and stay with us please?"

Daddy unlocked my fingers and picked me up off of his foot. He hugged me and told me that I couldn't go with him and that he couldn't stay. He once again told me to go back in the house. He said that he would watch me until I got back in and closed the door. I didn't want to leave Daddy, but that time I did what he said. I looked back at him one more time.

"Daddy, are you coming back home?"

Daddy looked at me, waved bye, got in the car and drove off. I went to the window and looked out to see him driving off. I repeated the question again to myself softly.

'Daddy, are you coming back?"

Unfortunately, that wouldn't be the last time I had to ask that question.

Let's Go Paint Today!

Beep! Beep! Beep! Beep! Beep!

The alarm clock was going off. This morning it seemed to be extra, extra loud though. I didn't know if it was because I was super sleepy or if it was normally that loud and I had never paid attention to it. Either way though, I rolled over to turn it off.

I guess I didn't hit it or didn't hit it hard enough the first time because it was still going off. Ughhhhh! I tried again. I hit it a little harder this time. Yes! Finally! No noise! I rolled back over and asked myself, '*Did I really want to get up and go paint today?*' I mean it was Saturday, which meant that I could have slept in if I wanted to. Saturdays were our lazy, clean up days. We slept in late, got up, ate cereal and cleaned up. After we finished cleaning, we watched cartoons for the rest of the day.

On this morning though, I really felt like I just needed a few more minutes to sleep. Just a couple more to get myself together. You see, I was not a morning person, especially not on a Saturday morning. We already had to get up early during the week to go to school. Saturdays were the only days we were able to really chill and relax.

Knock, knock!

Knock, knock!

"Ughhhhh, it's too early for this!"

Knock, knock!

Knock, knock!

I rolled my eyes as I rolled over to see who was at my door. It was probably nobody but Jamie.

"Who is it?" I asked with somewhat of an attitude.

"Jamie, duh!"

"Come in!"

"Makayla, girl why are you still in the bed? Aren't you still coming with us to paint that house today?"

"Yeah, I guess so," I said as I sighed and rolled my eyes.

"Well, get up. Unc said that he would be here in a few to get us!"

"Man, I really don't want to get up right now, Jamie. I'm still sleepy."

"Girl, get your butt up and get ready."

"Fine. I guess I can get up and get ready since I will be hanging out with your bad butt today."

"Girl, whatever. You better get up and get ready. He will be here any minute now!"

"Whatever!" I shouted as she walked out and slammed my door.

Man, it was bright in here. I knew that it was super early, but mercy it was so bright. It really was too early in the morning. I could barely open my eyes all the way. I thought to myself once again. '*Makayla, girl do you really want to get up right now?*' If I hadn't already told Jamie and

Uncle that I would come, I would have definitely still been asleep. Whelp, I guess I better get up and get ready for real this time.

I got up, stretched and yawned. I walked into the bathroom, turned on the water and started feeling around for my toothbrush. Where was my toothbrush? I knew that I put it back in the holder last night but I didn't see it. Hmmm, I couldn't leave the house with funky breath. That's a big no no. Mommy would have been like, "Child if you don't get your butt back in that bathroom and wash your face and brush your teeth."

I turned on the light. I guess I should have done that first instead of feeling around in the dark. It was sitting right there in the exact same place that I had left it. I had to wake up because I was tripping. I brushed my teeth, washed my face, threw on my pink shirt and blue jean overalls. I put lotion on my legs and feet and slipped on my white sandals with the pink flowers on them. I went downstairs and poured a big bowl of my favorite cereal, some good ole Fruity Pebbles. I ate other cereal, too, from time to time but these were my favorite.

Here came Jamie walking in. I could tell by the look on her face that she was about to start with the questions.

"Makayla, why do you have such a big bowl?

"Jamie, why don't you ever mind your business?

Both of us looked and rolled our eyes as we smirked at each other. She walked back out of the room. Jamie was my little cousin who thought that she was the boss of everyone, including me. Although she was my little cousin, we were the best of friends ever since I could remember.

On the weekends, we normally spent the night at each other's houses. This weekend, she spent the night at our house. We were going to paint with Jamie's mom's boyfriend. His name was Roger, but we always called him Uncle or Unc. Although he wasn't really our uncle, he and Auntie had been together for a while. So, the name just kind of stuck with him. He was really cool. He always gave us money or candy when we saw him. Today however, although I thought he was one of the coolest uncles, I wished he would have picked us up later. I slurped up the last little bit of milk, went over to the sink and rinsed my bowl. Jamie walked back into the kitchen.

"Hey Jamie, did Uncle happen to say how long we will be painting today?"

"No, he didn't say. He just told us to be ready by 7am. That way we wouldn't have to be there working all day."

"Oh okay. Question, so would you really be mad if I didn't go with y'all?"

"Uh, duh! Of course, I would be! I know it's early and everything cousin but please still come with us," she said as she stood there with her arms folded.

"Okay, okay, okay! I'm going to go. You're right, I'm just so sleepy. Hopefully, it won't take all day though!"

"Okay cool, Makayla. Are you about ready to go?"

"Yep, I guess so!"

Honk! Honk!

Honk! Honk!

Uncle is here right on time. We walked over to the door.

Uncle hollered, "Hey, are y'all girls ready yet?"

"Yeah, we are coming Unc!"

Jamie and I hopped in the truck and closed the door. It was an older truck, but we always liked riding in it. It made us feel like we were big girls because technically, we were sitting in the front. We looked out of the window and played "I Spy" or "Punch Buggies" during our rides. Today wasn't any different. We also played "Shame, Shame, Shame." When that was over, we just started talking. We were talking our little heads off. Before we realized it, we were already at the house.

We all hopped out of the truck, grabbed the supplies and walked up to the front door. Uncle took this big key ring out of his pocket, flipped through them for a minute and then opened the door. He went in first. Jamie and I followed after him.

Once inside, we put the supplies down by the front door and went on a small tour. After seeing the entire house, we went back to the front. Unc gave us instructions on where and what to paint. Jamie had the front bedroom and I had the bedroom across from the bathroom. All three of us took a paint tray and took it to the rooms that we were going to be painting. Uncle poured the paint in and then gave us a short demonstration on how to paint.

After Jamie and I got the hang of it, we all went into our separate rooms to get started. I went into the room that I was going to paint, looked around and thought hmmm, this shouldn't take too long. This room really wasn't too big. As a matter of fact, the house was a bit on the smaller side, which in my eyes meant that we wouldn't be there all day. Hopefully, we could make it back early enough to catch some cartoons and maybe go to the park. I grabbed my Walkman, put on my headphones, hit play and got started.

I was jamming and painting, painting and jamming. I broke out with The Running Man and yes all while still painting the walls. I must say, I did really well with my playlist this time. These songs had me in the zone. When I got ready to start on the second wall, I put the roller down and picked up the paint brush. I walked over by the window and started painting the trim. I was doing pretty good. I wondered how Jamie was doing and how much she had done so far. I hoped she was moving right along, just like me. I really didn't want to be there all day. I walked back over to the paint tray, put the brush back down and picked the roller up again. As soon as I stood back up to go back over to the window, I saw Unc out of the corner of my eye. I pushed pause on my Walk Man, slipped my headphones back on one side, looked up and said, "Yes Unc, do you need something?

"No Makayla, I was just checking in on you. You're doing a good job so far."

"Thank you, Unc! I thought that it was going to be hard but it's not hard at all."

Unc was walking around inspecting my work on the walls. He leaned in a couple of times to get a closer look at the walls, but then he started back inspecting. I really hoped the work was as good as he said it was. I couldn't tell by the faces he was making. When he leaned in, he raised his eyebrow as if he was in deep thought. I sure hoped that I didn't have to do everything over again.

"Makayla, come here for a second."

Big sigh, and here we go. "Yes Unc, did I mess something up?"

"No, you didn't mess anything up, but let me show you a couple of things. Do you see these little spots on the wall?"

"Yes, I see a couple of them."

"Okay, if you come across anymore spots like this, let me know before you paint over them so that I can go in and fill the hole first, okay?"

"Okay, I will let you know from now on."

"Okay cool. Keep up the good work. It looks great, Girlie! We will be finished in no time!"

"Thank you, Unc! I sure will."

I turned to go back over to the paint. I was so glad that Unc said that we should be finished early today. That meant we would have time to go back home, bathe and watch cartoons. I didn't think that we would go to the park though, because I was already tired.

I bent down, picked my roller up and dipped it in the paint. When I stood back up to start working, I noticed that Unc was still standing over by the door. It almost looked as if he was stuck. I thought he was going back out to finish his part or to check on Jamie.

I turned and said, "What's wrong, Unc?

"Oh, nothing is wrong. I'm just checking the door and the rest of the walls before I go and check Jamie's room. I saw a couple of small holes on the door that I need to patch before you paint."

"Oh, okay! I will wait until you get finished with it."

I turned and headed back towards the wall with the window. I was getting ready to start when I saw that he had closed the door, and this time he was coming towards me. I wondered what I had done. I sure hoped that I didn't mess anything up. I was doing it exactly how he had shown us when we first arrived.

"Makayla, come here for a second. I see that you were working on the windows and baseboards. Let me show you how to paint them correctly before I go into the other room, okay?"

"Sure Unc," I said, as I was trying to hand him the roller.

I was a little confused because he didn't take the roller. Instead, he came right up behind me. He put his hand up on the wall, which caused me to be wedged between him and the wall.

"Ummm, Uncle! Here you go. Let me get out of your way so that I can see what you are doing."

He didn't respond. He just stood there. It was almost like he was staring off in space. I wondered what he was looking at. The space on the wall that he was looking at seemed to look okay.

"Hey Uncle. Can you please stand beside me and show me how to do it? Or can I watch you do it and then try it? That way you can tell me if it is right or not."

Still there was no answer. By this time, Unc had pressed his body up against mine. Now my back was against the wall. I couldn't tell what he was doing because he wasn't saying anything. He just stood there with a blank look on his face, and he was starting to breathe kind of funny. I wondered if something had happened to him. I hoped he didn't die. My mommy was a nurse. Although she would know what to do, it would take too long for her to get here. I tried to wiggle my way from between him and the wall, but I was stuck.

"Hey Unc?"

"Uncle?"

"Hey Unc, can you move back some so that I can move please?"

Still no answer. Again, he just stood with no facial expression, no words, nothing.

"Hello? Unc? Can you move please?

Again, he still didn't answer. Instead, he took his hand and stroked it against my cheek. His hand moved from my cheek and down to my neck. I tried pulling my face away when all of a sudden, I felt his hands tighten around my neck. I was so afraid. I didn't know why he had just grabbed me by my neck. If he was mad about the paint, I could have just fixed it. He didn't have to grab me. I was only a little girl. I could repaint it.

"Uncle?" I mumbled.

"What are you doing? You are hurting me," I said as I was trying to get his hand from around my neck.

"Please Unc, please let me go. You are hurting me! Can you let me go please?"

Still, there was no response. Not one word. His grip around my neck tightened to the point that it was getting hard to breathe. I started coughing, which made him loosen up, but just a tad bit. I was able to take a deep breath, so I tried begging him to let me go again.

"Unc, please move! You are hurting me? I could barely breathe."

He took his hand off of my neck and shoved my head into the wall. At this point, I was terrified. I didn't know what he was doing or going to do. I couldn't understand how he was just telling me that I was doing a good job with painting and now this? Was it something that he saw on the door that was making him so mad? What did I do that was so wrong? He had my head pressed so hard against the wall that I thought it was going to go through it. As he held my head down with one hand, he took his other hand and shoved it down and into the front of my overalls.

"Uncle, PLEASE LET ME GO! What are you doing? Please move your hand! Mommy told me that that's my private part and NO ONE is allowed to touch it! PLEASE STOPPPPP!"

I didn't understand why he was doing this to me. I was just a little girl. But that didn't matter to him because my tears went unnoticed. My cries went unheard. I tried to push him away, but he was just too strong. I almost felt as if my feet had left the floor and I was pinned to the wall by my head.

The next thing I knew, somehow, he had spread my legs apart with his leg. He was pulling on my panties. I guess he was trying to move them to the side but ended up ripping them. I was just dangling there in shock. What was my Uncle doing to me and why?

"Uncle, can you please STOP and put me down? I'm sorry if I messed up with painting. I will fix it! I promise I will fix it. Just please STOP!"

I was still trying to fight him off. I just wanted him to move his hands and put me down. I didn't understand. All of this because I painted something wrong? He had really gone crazy.

"SSSSSTTTTTOOOOOPPPPP!!"

I was screaming as loud as I could, but he put his hand that was holding my head against the wall over my mouth. My screams became muffled noises. I heard him whisper, "Shut up before I give you something to cry for." I just looked at him and wondered what else could possibly be worse than this?

All of a sudden, I felt this horrible burning sensation as he shoved his fingers inside of me. It felt as if he was ripping me to shreds down there. It was hurting so badly. He shoved his fingers in and slid them out repeatedly. The pain was almost unbearable. I begged and pleaded with him to stop, but he was not listening.

I knew that what he was doing was wrong because Mommy always told me that no one should ever touch me down there, but he was and he wouldn't stop. Why couldn't he just let me go? It felt as if he was punching me in my stomach and my private part. With all the pain that I was feeling, I didn't know what was hurting more, my head, my stomach or my private area. I just couldn't believe that he was doing what he was doing to me.

"Please, please, please let me go! You are really hurting me Uncle. What have I done to you? I'm sorry that I painted over the holes without telling you! I didn't know that it would make you so mad! I promise I will fix it. Please, just stop now and I will fix it! I promise. Please just please stop hurting me!"

Still, he didn't say a word. I continued crying until he finished shoving his fingers in and out of me. When he had finished, he took the hand that he had in me and put it down into his pants to where his private part was. All the while, my head was still pressed into the wall.

"Please let me go! Please! You are really hurting me!"

He still didn't answer. He just started moving the hand that was in his pants up and down. I didn't know what he was doing, but he was starting to make these weird grunting noises. He almost sounded like a dog and a pig mixed together. It was such an awful sound. He was moving his hand up and down in his pants where his private area was. He moved it fast and then slow, fast and slow until he let out this big, long moan. I thought he may have hurt himself, so I tried once again to get him to put me down. But, the more I fought, the harder he pushed my head into the wall. My head was hurting badly. My head had never hurt like that before.

Please God, please make him stop. Please! I just want Mommy and Daddy. I didn't know why Uncle was doing what he did, but I just wanted to go home. I wanted to get as far away from him as I possibly could. I was so afraid and confused. I thought to myself, if he squeezed or pushed any harder, I was going to die right there. I didn't know how to get him to let go of me.

For a minute, he was quiet. Then he leaned his face in closer to me until his face was literally touching mine. I felt the sweat from his forehead on mine. I felt his breath in my ear, as I heard him whisper.

"If you tell anyone and I mean anyone Makayla, I WILL KILL YOU! Do you hear me little girl? You know that I know where you all live. Don't play with me! Do you hear me?"

"Yes!" I cried.

"If you think that I'm playing, try me! I will come and shoot and kill everyone! But you, Makayla, I will really mess you up if I hear anything!"

My heart was beating so fast. Why would he want to kill me when he was the one who hurt me? He hurt my private part and Mommy said no one should touch my little girl area. Why I am going to die over painting the room the wrong way?

"Did you hear what I said girl?"

"Yes, I heard you," I mumbled.

"I'm not playing with your little ugly ass! You do know that you wanted me to do this to you right? I could see it in your eyes."

"Wait! Huh? I didn't want you to touch me Uncle. I didn't ask you to do anything except show me how to paint!"

"Yes, you did girl. Coming over here with those little overall shorts on. You were practically begging me to show you how a real man feels."

I couldn't do anything but cry even more. I was so confused. I'm only eight. Why would I need to know what a "real" man feels like? I was a child. I just wanted to help him and my cousin paint. How could I have asked him to hurt me when I was begging him to stop hurting me? My private area was hurting so badly.

Finally, he let go of my head and I dropped down to the floor and continued crying. I just couldn't believe what happened. I couldn't stop shaking. Why did he do that to me? What did he mean that I asked for it by what I had on? I just didn't get it.

Once he left out of the room, I waited a few minutes to make sure that he wasn't outside the door. When it felt like he was gone, I ran to the bathroom and locked the door. I cried and cried and cried some more. I couldn't stop crying and shaking. I just couldn't seem to wrap my head around what just happened. Why did he do this to me? Would he really kill my family? I love Mommy, Daddy, my sisters and brother. I didn't want anything to happen to them. I wanted to go home so badly. I had to try and get myself together.

I turned on the water and tried to wash the paint off my face and clothes, but it wouldn't come off. I stood there looking in that bathroom mirror with tears still falling from my eyes. The paint on the side of my face and on my clothes was a horrible reminder of what took place.

I kept looking in the mirror asking myself, "Am I really ugly? I've not heard anyone tell me that I was pretty or beautiful, so maybe I am ugly. I don't want to be ugly anymore God. Ugly girls get treated so badly.

Is this what happens to ugly little girls who wear overalls? I swear I hate overalls now! I don't ever want to wear them again. They make uncles hurt little girls' private parts. Overalls are so stupid.

I tried sitting down to use the bathroom. OMG. I was burning and hurting down there. I just buried my head in my hands and cried again. I got up and tried to wipe. There was red stuff on the tissue. I had never seen any color or anything red when I wiped before. OMG. He broke my private part. I had to tell Mommy that he hurt and broke me down there.

"Dear God, please fix my broken part. I don't think that it is supposed to have red stuff coming out. Please God, I don't know what to do. I want to tell Mommy and Daddy, but I don't want them to die. Please don't let my family die God! Amen!"

I didn't know how long I had been sitting in the bathroom. I was trying my best to stop crying, but I couldn't seem to stop. Why did I even get out of bed this morning? Why did I even come help him paint today? Why did this happen to me? I'm just a little girl!

Knock, Knock!

Knock, Knock!

At the sound of the knock on the door, I was immediately struck with fear. It almost paralyzed me. I didn't want to make a sound. I feared that Uncle was coming back in to hurt me again. I was already in so much pain. I was trying to stop crying and get myself together, but if he was back to hurt me again what would I do?

"Yes?" I answered softly.

"Makayla, are you ok? You have been in there for a long time," asked Jamie.

I sighed the biggest sigh of relief. I thought I would hear Uncle's voice coming from the other side of the door. I was sitting there trembling in fear. I even think I stopped breathing for a second. I took a deep breath before I responded to Jamie.

"I'm okay Jamie. I will be out in a few minutes. My stomach is hurting, so I am trying to use the bathroom."

"Ewww, you in there taking a dump, aren't you? You so nasty Makayla! This is not our house. Get out of there, girl!" she said as she laughed.

"Ah, hush girl! I am not doing #2. I will be out in a few!"

If she only knew what just happened, what I was going through and feeling right then. I wanted to just cry on her shoulder but didn't want to answer any of the million and one questions that she would have asked. I also didn't want her to die because of me either.

I just sat in the bathroom trying to figure out what to do. I'm only a little girl and an ugly one at that. Who would believe me? Would he really kill my entire family? I didn't know what to do. I cried for a while longer, got up, washed my hands, wiped my face and walked out of the bathroom.

"Jamie?"

"Jamie?"

"Where are you?"

I started getting a little nervous as I was looking in the rooms for Jamie. She didn't say anything when I called her name. I didn't see or hear her, so I went back up towards the front of the house in the room where she had been painting. When I got to the door, it opened. I immediately froze.

It was Uncle coming out of the room that Jamie was in. He walked out, put his hand on my shoulder and whispered, "You remember what I said with your ugly ass right?" as he walked past me. I couldn't even answer or say anything, so I just nodded my head.

I stepped in the room and looked around. Jamie was sitting over in front of the window. She was curled up like a baby. I walked over to her.

"Jamie?"

"Jamie?"

"Jamie, are you okay? Please answer me!"

She did not say a word. She just looked up at me with her big brown eyes and I just knew. No, no, no, please God! Please tell me that he didn't do the same thing to her. She was younger than me. My poor cousin. Uncle was such a mean and horrible man. He had always seemed so nice when he would come over.

"Jamie, are you okay?"

"Jamie, are you okay? Please say something!"

I walked over to tap her on the shoulder. She was sitting there shaking. I felt for her because from the way she was acting, I could tell that Uncle hurt her, too.

"Jamie!"

She looked up at me with tears in her eyes and said, "I want to go home right now! I don't want to paint anymore Makayla!"

I knew at that very moment that he hurt her, and I just couldn't believe it. Not my little cousin, too. I picked her up from the floor and we both walked out to the truck and got in.

Neither one of us said a word, not one word the entire way home. Jamie and I just held each other's hands while we sat in silence. I thought to myself, if he did the same thing to her as he did to me, I knew that she was hurting and in pain, too. I wanted to ask her but not in front of him. I didn't want anything else to happen to us. I could tell by the look in her eyes that something was not right.

We pulled up to my house. As soon as he stopped, we jumped out of the truck. We both ran as fast as we could into the house. As we slammed the door behind us, I heard him calling us. I didn't want to, but I looked out of the window. Uncle was sitting there holding out his hand as if he was pointing a gun. I turned back around and yanked Jamie out of the window.

"Hey girls, how did it go with painting today?" Mommy asked.

"It was okay," I said as I walked to the bathroom.

I sat on the edge of the tub while the water ran. The only thing that I could ask myself was why? Why me? Why us? Why did this happen? Was Jamie okay? Why did I even get out of the bed this morning? I should have just said that I didn't want to go. I don't ever want to paint again.

A Walk Through the Park

"Jocelyn, girl if you don't turn the TV back to that channel. You know I was watching that movie."

"Dang Makayla. I didn't know that it was that serious. You do know that you're at my house and not yours though, right?"

I couldn't do anything but roll my eyes. After all, she was telling the truth. But I was so into the movie that we were watching though. When she changed the channel, I sat up on that bed so quick. I didn't even realize that I had caught an attitude.

It's just that, well, you know how it is when you're into a movie and you can tell that something really good is about to happen or go down? Yep, that's how I was feeling at that moment. Like I was about to miss something. Lord knows my stomach was already in knots from the anticipation. When it's good like that, you don't want anyone talking, turning the channel or getting in the way. I was literally glued to the TV.

"My bad girl, it was getting to the good part. I just didn't want to miss anything. You know how it is!"

"Whatever Kay! Don't let it happen again!"

I just sat there, smirked and rolled my eyes at the same time. She said that I was the one with the attitude but hers was worse than mine. Jocelyn and I were friends ever since we moved into the neighborhood a few years back. She was sweet as pie but she definitely did not play. Although she could be feisty at times, I wouldn't have traded her for anything in the world.

"Anyways, may I get something to drink please? I'm super thirsty."

"You lucky you are my girl, Kay. Or you would be getting it yourself," Jocelyn said as she walked out of the room.

I laid back down across the bed, looked out the window and started thinking. '*Man, it's actually pretty nice outside. Maybe when the movie is over, we can walk down to the park or go to the gym and see what's going on there. Something, especially since the weather has been so crazy lately.*'

Jocelyn was heading back to the room. She walked up to me and shoved the glass into my hand. This girl right her! But I'm the one with the 'tude. Whew, yeah right! She almost jammed my finger the way she shoved that glass in my hand. Well, maybe I'm over exaggerating but geesh, who had the attitude now?

"Dang, not so rough Joc!"

"Ummm, you are welcome!"

"Uh huh. Thank you! With your mean self!"

"Uh huh, yeah you're welcome Kay!"

"Yeah, yeah, yeah! Anyways, girl, didn't I tell you this movie was good?"

"You were right! I can't lie. It was a really good movie!"

"See, I told you."

"Any who, Kay, what you want to do now?"

"I was thinking about that a minute ago. Hmmm, what about the park? You want to go down there and see if anyone is there?"

"Makayla, girl stop playing. Now you know I'm not going outside or walking for that matter! It's too hot!"

"Well dang Joc, tell me how you really feel. Geesh. What do you want to do then?"

"You want to watch another movie?"

"Not really. It's nothing really on TV."

"I know, right? It's never anything on TV."

"It's cool. I need to be making my way home anyway. You know how Mommy is."

"Yes, I do. You know your mom don't be playing Kay! You better get home before you get a whooping."

"Whatever! You always trying to be funny. Anyways, I will see you later girl."

"Bye girl. See you later. Don't get no whooping."

Although she was telling the truth, I was not about to let her know. My mommy was crazy. I didn't feel like hearing anything today. Better to get home early rather than run the risk of being late. Man, let me tell you, if those street lights came on and we were not in the house! Well, let's just say that is a totally different story. I just didn't have time for it today.

So, I left from Jocelyn's house (and yes, I left early) and headed home. I was just glad that she didn't stay too far away from me. Although it was beautiful outside, I really didn't feel like walking and I was glad that Joc didn't want to hang out anywhere. The walk itself wasn't that long, but since I was tired, it seemed as if the road had gotten longer. It's funny that while I was laying there watching the movie, I wasn't tired. But, as soon as I got outside and started to head home, it hit me. I was ready to get home, but I kind of wanted a snack also.

There was a corner store in between Joc's house and mine. I figured since it was on the way that I'd run in and grab a snack or two before I got home. My usual bag of chips, a Twix and a bottle of Cheerwine sounded really good at that moment. '*Hopefully they have the Cheerwine in stock*,' I thought to myself as I walked into the store.

Calvin, the cashier, was behind the counter. He was a little older than me and seemed pretty cool. We always made small talk when I came in the store. He was finishing up with a customer when I walked in, but I saw him look up and give me a nod. I went over by the fridge and grabbed a drink. I heard him tell the customer that he would see them next time.

"Hey Makayla. How are you today, Girlie?"

"I'm doing good Calvin. How are you?"

"Doing pretty good. Just ready to go as usual."

"That's good. What time you getting off today?"

"I get off at 5 pm and I'm running out of here as soon as the clock strikes 5, too!"

"I heard that."

I couldn't help but giggle as I thought about him taking off so fast. All I knew was, he better look both ways before crossing that street. No time for accidents.

"So, what are you doing with yourself today Girlie?"

"Nothing at all. Just left Jocelyn's house and about to head home. Had to stop in to get my usual though."

"Oh, okay cool. Sounds good. Let me guess, Twix, chips and Cheerwine, right?"

"You already know it. Thank you."

"Cool. $1.85, please."

"Here you go. I will see you next time, okay Cal. Don't work too hard."

"Okay Makayla. You know I won't. Have a good one!"

"You do the same!"

I walked out wandering if I should eat my snacks before I got home? I really didn't feel like sharing. If I went to my house with snacks, I would have to give everybody some. I definitely didn't feel like sharing that day. Nope, not that day! That day, these were all mine! I headed to the park and sat on the swings and ate, since the park was right up the street from my house.

I started walking towards my house again. I was approaching the park. As I opened the wrapper of my Twix, I heard someone calling my name. I stopped, turned to look around but couldn't tell who it was, so I started walking again.

"Aye Makayla!"

I stopped, turned, squinted my eyes. Oh, Lord. It was Reggie, but everyone called him Redd. He was dating a friend of mine named Tiffany. He was a lot older than everyone else, but he always hung out with us and kids younger than him. I never understood why but I guess it was because of Tiffany. He was tall, brown, with a medium build with curly hair. Most of the time he seemed out of place, but maybe that's just how I saw him.

"Oh, what's up Redd. How's it going with you?"

"It's going pretty good, Girlie. How about you? What you getting into today?"

"Nothing much. Just left Joc's house, about to head home. What you doing up here?"

"Cool, cool! I'm just chilling. Sitting here waiting on Tiffany to meet me."

"That's what's up. Where she at?"

"She's at home, but she should be up here in a few minutes or so. You know how y'all girls do."

"Whatever Redd! Y'all going out tonight or just chilling?"

"Nah, not tonight. We are just going to chill in the park and maybe grab something to eat a little later."

"Okay cool, well I'm on the way to the house so I will see you later. Tell Tiffany I said "hey and to call me later!"

Whelp, that just ruined my plans. I know I said that I was going to sit at the park and eat my chips and candy, but I really didn't feel like talking and especially not to him. Even though he was my friend's boyfriend, I always thought that he seemed a little creepy. For one, he was old, like 29 or so, which was definitely old to me. Two, whenever we were at Tiffany's house, he always stared at me. It made me so uncomfortable to the point where sometimes I left and went home. So, I did not want to sit and have a conversation with him and especially not by myself.

"Wait, hold on Makayla. Come here for a second."

I rolled my eyes and sighed as I turned back towards him. Like, what could he possibly have wanted? I was literally just standing in front of him. He could have asked or said whatever he had to then! I know it may have seemed like I'm over reacting, but I just didn't feel like being bothered and not by him of all people. All I wanted to do was eat my snacks, drink my soda and go home.

"What's up, Redd?"

"Aye Kay, you want to make some money really quick?"

"What do you mean 'make some money?' 'Make some money' how?"

"Listen Girlie, do you want to make some money or not?"

Oh no, he didn't! How could he have an attitude? We were literally just standing here chatting and he didn't say nor did he ask me what he needed to ask me. Then when I started to walk off, he wanted to ask me a question. But when I asked questions, then he wanted to get aggy. Like seriously dude? I was so ready to get to the house. I knew I should've kept walking when I saw that it was him, but no, I had to be polite.

"Again, how would I make some money, Redd?"

If he didn't get whatever it was out so that I could be on my way, I was walking away. It was hot! My Twix had already started melting. I was going to be pissed if I had to throw my candy away. It was not often that I had something to myself with my sisters and brothers at home.

"Again, do you want to make some money, Kay?"

I was confused and getting really agitated because by that time, I felt like he was playing games. It was a simple question. How was I supposed to make money? All I knew was that he better not ask me to do anything stupid! I hope he didn't want me to go on a drug run or shoplifting for him. That was surely not about to happen. I was definitely not about that life. I was not about to go to jail for anyone or anything. I couldn't say for sure or not if he sold drugs, but he seemed as if he did.

"Makayla! Girl! Quit tripping! Do you want to make some money or not?"

"Again, how would I be making this so-called money, Redd? What would I have to do and how much would I get?"

"I will give you $200 if you're trying to make some money! So, are you down or not Girlie?"

"$200 for what? You still aren't answering my question Redd! I can't give you an answer until you tell me what I would have to do!"

I don't think that he was used to anyone asking him questions.

Normally, he would flash his money around and the girls would flock to him. Not me, though. His flashing his money didn't do anything for me. I wasn't about to do anything just because he showed some cash. I needed details. If it was going to cause me to endanger my life or go to jail, I was not having it. I was just a child.

By this time, I was standing in front of him with my arms folded like come on, spit it out already. I guess he could tell I was getting aggravated because he stood up and walked a little closer to me. I took a few steps back because he got a little too close. I guess he knew nothing about personal space.

"Listen girl, you know that I have had my eye on you for a while now right? I'm just trying to put a little change in your pocket."

"Ummm no, I didn't know that at all! Aren't you and Tiffany together? And $200 is not a little change, Sir!"

"Quit tripping, Kay! Yeah, we are together but that doesn't mean that I haven't been feeling you though."

"Okay, so, yeah, that's not cool at all! Listen, I'm about to head home. Have fun with Tiffany, you know, your girlfriend, when she gets here!"

The nerve of this dude, talking about he is feeling me. That is so not cool. I wondered if Tiffany knew that he was "feeling" other girls. She really liked him. I would know because that's all she would talk about when we would hang out.

"Makayla, wait! Hang on a second. For real!"

"Oh my gosh! What is it?"

"Don't be like that Girlie. Okay! Listen, can I just touch you? That's all I'm asking is to just touch on you. You don't have to do anything but stand there. Just one time and just for a minute."

"Wait, say what now? You want to touch me and for $200? You're not even making any sense."

"Kay, I don't want to have sex. I just want to touch you, you know, down there."

"Man, have you lost your mind? This conversation is over!"

I turned to walk away from him. I wanted to get as far away from him and as quickly as I could. Before I could turn all the way around, he grabbed my shoulder, which stopped me. I was getting so pissed off. I could have sworn that I just told him that he couldn't touch me. That included on the shoulder as well. What was wrong with this man? I jerked my shoulder away from him.

"Come on Girlie, it will be quick. I promise. Besides, you know that Tiffany is on her way up here. So, you know I can't be too long. Please Kay? I got the money right here!"

"Listen Man, you are not about to be touching or feeling on me in any type of way with your old nasty self. You do know that I'm 13, right? Besides, don't you have a girlfriend that you can do that with? You done bumped your head for real. I'm leaving."

"Makayla, I don't even want to put it in you. I just want to rub it on you for a few minutes. Girl, you know you need some money. Everybody can use a little money. That's all you have to do to get this $200. Now come on and stop playing!"

"Wait, what? You want to do what? So first you said touch, now you are saying that you just want to rub it on me? Nope, that's not happening! Just rub it on your girl. She will be here in a few minutes anyway."

Man, I couldn't believe that he had really asked me some stupid mess like that. What was he thinking? Maybe it worked with other girls, but I'm not them. I don't need money that bad. He needs to go and get one of those other girls or heck, even one of those prostitutes who walks around at night.

This man was crazy for real. I knew there was a reason I thought he was creepy and here it was. I was so over the whole conversation. I wanted to get as far away from him and as fast as I possibly could. Something was seriously wrong with him.

I turned to walk away again. Before I knew it, he grabbed me but this time it was by my wrist. He yanked me back towards him and I almost fell. He pulled me so hard that I thought my arm was going to go flying through the air. I couldn't believe he just yanked my arm the way he did. He had me by my wrist with one hand and with the other one, he had started unzipping his pants.

"Redd, STOP! Let me go NOW! Didn't I already tell you that you couldn't touch me?" I screamed.

He ignored me and just continued doing what he was doing like I was not yelling in his face and trying to get away from him. I kept screaming and asking him to let me go, but he wouldn't let up on his grip.

"Redd, let me go! I don't want you nor your money!"

By this time, he was holding himself down there, but he was holding it up towards me. All I could do was cry and plead with him to stop. He still had a grip on my arm and had pulled me in even closer to him. He was trying his best to get in between my legs to rub on my private part. I was terrified and sick to my stomach, all at the same time.

Why couldn't I have just kept on walking, always trying to be polite and not hurt anyone's feelings. This was one time that would have been okay to ignore someone. God, please help me get away from this monster.

"Redd, please let my arm go! You are hurting me!

Still nothing. Not one word. He didn't even look at me. It was like he was someone or something else. If anyone had met him at that moment, they would have said that he was a monster with no soul.

"Oh my God, Redd, can you please put your thang back up. I said NO! I already told you that you couldn't touch me or rub it on me! Now let me go!"

I was trying to fight him off, but he just pulled me in closer to him. I didn't know how he was able to grab me by my hair. I felt my hair being ripped as his grip tightened. I tried to pull his fingers away from my hair. It didn't work. He just tightened his grip on my hair with one hand and grabbed me by my throat with his other hand. I heard him whispering in my ear.

"Didn't I tell you that this wouldn't take long. Chill out, let me finish and I'll let you go."

Please God! Please don't let this happen again. I don't want to go through this. I just want to go home. I promise. I will share all my food from now on. Please, just make him let me go, God. Please!

I was still trying to get away. He was trying to force his leg in between my legs to pry them open. The more I refused, the harder he pulled my hair. Once again, I felt my hair being ripped from my scalp. I was trying my best to fight him off and break away from him, but he was so strong.

When he couldn't get his leg in between mine, he started pulling on my shorts. He almost ripped my shorts and panties apart trying to pull them to the side. I didn't know what was hurting more now, my head or my private part. It felt as if he was giving me a wedgy but in the private area instead of the back. Man, I was hurting so badly.

All of a sudden, I felt the tip of his thang touch me down there and I thought for sure that he was about to rape me. I felt so defeated. So afraid. I did not want to go through this. I screamed even louder. "Please God, no!" All I could think was why was this happening? Again? I didn't want him touching me! Why wouldn't he listen?

"Nooooo, Redd, please let me go! Please don't do this! I said NO! I told you that I did not want you to touch me! You cannot have sex with me! Your girlfriend will be here any minute, remember? Please get your hands off of my butt! Please, stopppppppp! LEAVE ME ALONE!"

Why was he not listening? I knew that he could hear me because I was literally screaming right in his face. It was like he tuned me out or blacked out or something. All I knew was that he was not listening. Like, was I talking to a brick wall or something? I was begging and pleading with him but it seemed to have fallen on deaf ears. I was fighting, pulling away, screaming, but nothing seemed to work.

I was still trying to fight him off, but he was trying to lift one of my legs up so that he could shove his thang inside of me. This cannot be happening! I just can't go through this again! He tried lifting it higher but when he did, I lost my balance and fell to the ground.

When I fell, I started kicking and pushing myself backwards and away from him, but he still managed to get a kick in before I could get away from him. It was almost as if I was butt crawling, but it didn't matter to me. Anything that I could do to get away from this monster, I was going to do it. It didn't matter that I was scooting in the dirt. I was just happy to have broken free from his grip.

I was able to back up far enough so I could stand up. As soon as I was getting on my feet, all I heard was him yelling and screaming at me. I was confused. He was just trying to rape me, but he was mad at me? I was trying to catch my breath while still backing up. I wanted to make sure that I kept him at a distance.

"Makayla? Why are you acting like that, girl? You know your little ugly tail need some money! Who else you know going to give you some money for doing nothing? That's all you are good for anyways. You might as well get back over here and let me finish so you can get this money."

Wait? Did he really just call me ugly? All because I didn't want to let him "touch me?" I didn't get it. I didn't ask him for his money nor did I need it, especially enough to be touched, molested or raped by him with his nasty self. Oh my God, I knew that he was creepy, but I didn't think that he was so freaking disgusting. I couldn't believe what he had just tried to do. I mean what he and Tiffany did when they were alone was their business. I didn't want any parts of that mess.

By that time, I had caught my breath. I was standing straight up when I saw that he was trying to come closer to me. I took off running as fast as I could. I was determined to make it home to my mommy. While I was running, I could hear that he was still hollering.

"Forget you, Makayla! Don't nobody want your ole stupid ugly tail anyways. I was just trying to put some money in your pocket but you tripping. You better not tell Tiffany! You know I know where you stay! Don't make me have to come to your house. It will be a wrap for you and your family! You better not let me hear that you have said anything to anyone or I will kill you!"

Those statements stopped me dead in my tracks. I was immediately struck with fear again when I heard him say that. What did my family have to do with this? All of this because I didn't want him to touch me? I couldn't do anything but start back running and crying. What was probably only about a minute or so seemed like forty-five minutes to an hour.

I finally reached my porch and man, I was scared and out of breath! I was trying to slow my breathing down and get myself together before I went in the house, but the more I thought about it the more upset I became.

God, why me? What did I do wrong? I just couldn't understand why this kept happening? Was it me? Was it something that I was doing? I was only trying to walk through the park to eat my snacks. I guess that's what I got for being greedy.

Did this really only happen to ugly little girls? I mean, no one ever told me that I was beautiful so maybe I was ugly. I didn't think that I was that ugly though. Not ugly enough to keep going through that. God, why couldn't I have been beautiful and pretty like everyone else? If I was pretty, I bet I wouldn't have to keep going through these situations?

Why didn't they stop when I asked them to? Better yet, why did they pick me in the first place? What was wrong with me God? Why did you make me so ugly? You hated me too, huh?

I tried to stop crying so that I could walk in the house, but I couldn't. I was afraid, hurting and sad. I wanted to go inside, but I didn't want to go inside, if that made any sense. I knew that if I went inside, my mommy would ask me what was wrong. How could I tell her what just happened?

Redd did say that he knew where we stayed. And if I told anyone he would kill my family and me. How could I tell Mommy? I didn't want my family to die. I couldn't believe that he threatened my family and me.

Oh, my goodness, would he really ride by my house? Would he really hurt my family or me? My heart was beating so hard and so fast.

I had to try and catch my breath so I could finally go in the house. Deep breath in. Deep breath out. Deep breath in. Deep breath out. I was trying to compose myself as I walked up to the door.

As I was about to put the key in, I heard a car going down the street. I could have literally peed on myself right then and there I was so scared. I wanted to turn around but couldn't. Was that him? Was he coming to hurt us already? I didn't want to die. I just stood at the door shaking.

The car passed our house and I almost collapsed. My nerves were shot. This couldn't be my life. I didn't want to look over my shoulder for the rest of my life.

I put the key in the door and turned the knob. I took a quick look over both of my shoulders just to make sure that I didn't see him before entering. I walked in, closed and locked the door. I stood there looking out of the window just to make sure that he wasn't coming. After a while, when I didn't see him coming, I looked through the house to see if anyone was home. No one was home yet. I didn't know if I was relieved that no one was home for me to have to explain myself to, or if I was sad and hurt that no was there to tell me that everything was going to be okay. Either way, I didn't think that I would have been able to explain to them what just happened or why I had been crying. I went to my room and plopped down in the floor. I broke down crying again. I just couldn't stop. I sat there crying and in a daze.

I couldn't believe what happened to me, again! Something had to give. Not only did he try to molest and rape me, but I was called ugly again. I started to think that may have been true. Was I really that ugly? All I was simply trying to do was take a walk through the park to eat my snacks before I got home. I guess that was my punishment for not wanting to share. I should have just kept walking straight home. Man, I hate the park!

But I Almost Drowned Though!

Today was the day and I was so excited! Not only was today the last day of my summer work program, but it was also Pool Day! I worked all summer. It wasn't hard work but office work. I filed papers, stapled them, made copies, etc. Whatever Mrs. Sullivan asked me to do, I did it right away. Even though I was still a little too young to work, I was able to work in the Youth Summer Program. I worked for a hours a couple of days a week. I was probably more excited than when I first started. We were told that on the last day of the program, everyone who participated would go swimming.

I absolutely loved the water. I was an okay swimmer but just being in the water made me happy. My family and I didn't get to go often but when we did, I always had a blast! It was something that just tickled me about running and jumping into the pool. I couldn't really dive in that well. It always seemed to turn into a belly flop, which could be a little painful. So, I just did cannonballs most of the time.

I could even do flips and headstands while in the water. I remember this one time I ran and tried to flip into the pool and hit my head on the side. I said from that point on that I would only do flips while in the water. That was definitely not a fun experience for me.

I was just so excited to be going swimming on the last day. Before I went to work, I packed a bag with my bathing suit, towel and extra clothes. I was ready for some fun in the sun.

"Makayla, are you ready to go?"

"Yes, Mommy, I'm ready to go! You remember that I'm going swimming today, right?"

"Yes, child! How could I forget? That's all that you have been talking about all week. Do you have everything in your bag?"

"Yes, I have everything!"

"Okay, well let's go then. I don't want you to miss your last day."

Mommy and I walked out the door, locked it and went to the car. I couldn't wait to arrive work. Well, I couldn't wait for it to be over, I should say. The ride seemed to take forever. It seemed as if we were stuck at every red light there was. Finally, we made it. I got ready to hop out of the car when Mommy stopped me.

"Makayla, slow down child! Don't forget to grab your bag. What time do I need to pick you up?"

"Sorry Mommy, I was so excited that I almost left it in the car. I think they said we will be ready by 6pm. You want me to run in and ask Mrs. Sullivan before you leave?"

"Yes, go in and ask her. I want to make sure that your Daddy or I will be here on time to pick you up."

"Okay Mommy, I'll be right back."

I grabbed my bag and hopped out of the car. I walked into the building and put my things down at my desk. I said, "Good morning" to a few other people that were there before I saw Mrs. Sullivan.

"Good morning, Mrs. Sullivan. How are you doing?"

"I'm doing well this morning, Makayla. Thank you. Are you ready to get your day started?"

"Yes, I am! I am so excited about going swimming today. I have all of my stuff with me. Mommy wanted me to ask you what time I need to be picked up today?"

"That's great. Tell your mother that we will be back here at 6pm."

"That's what I told her, but she wanted me to double check just to make sure so that she or Daddy will be here on time. She is outside waiting on me to confirm the time. I will be right back."

"Okay, Makayla!"

I ran back outside to our car.

"Mrs. Sullivan said that we will be back here at 6pm, Mommy. I will see you later."

"Okay Makayla, your Daddy or I will be here to pick you up tonight. Have fun and I will see you later."

"Okay, Mommy."

I heard Mommy driving off as I walked back into the building. I returned to my desk and put my things away. I was ready to get started. We were only working for a couple hours in the office today, since we were going to the pool later. I walked out of the office to look for Mrs. Sullivan and get my list of duties for the day.

"Hey Makayla!

"Hey Chase. How are you?

"I'm doing great! Are you ready for the pool today?"

"Yeah, I sure am. I'm packed and ready to go! I'm just trying to find Mrs. Sullivan to see what all she needs me to do. Have you seen her?"

"Yeah, she is in her office!"

"Okay, thank you, Chase!"

Knock, knock!

Knock, knock!

"Yes, come in!"

"Mrs. Sullivan, what do you need me to do today?"

Mrs. Sullivan gave me a huge stack of papers to separate and file. I was also given another stack to copy. I went into the file room and began to work. Although I was paying attention to what I was doing, I wasn't too focused, if that made sense. My mind was totally on the pool and trying to get there.

I finished my work in no time. I asked my other friends that were in the summer work program if they needed any help with anything. No one needed help, so I returned to Mrs. Sullivan's office to see if there was anything else for me to do.

I walked to her office. The door was already open, but she wasn't in it. I turned to go back to my desk when I saw Mr. Davis walking towards me.

Mr. Davis worked for the company that sponsored our program. He didn't seem to be that old. Well, at least not as old as the other people that worked there. He was very friendly and nice to all of us in the program. He was pretty cool.

"Hey, Makayla. How are you doing today? Are you ready to go to the pool?"

"Hey, Mr. Davis. Yes, I sure am! Do you know what time we are leaving?

"Great! We should be leaving here in just a few! Have you finished all of your work?"

"Yeah, I have. I asked everyone if they needed any help and they didn't." I looked in Mrs. Sullivan's office, but she wasn't in there. "Have you seen her?"

"Well, look at you trying to get everything done and out of the way! Way to go, Makayla! I'm not sure where she is, but I'm sure she is around here somewhere."

"Okay, I will wait at my desk until she comes and gets me."

I returned to my desk and sat down. I was bored out of my mind just sitting there. I got up and started straightening up the room. I moved some boxes around and stacked them in the corner. I was in the corner when I heard Mrs. Clarke call my name.

"Makayla, everyone has finished their work. Go ahead and get your things together. We will be leaving in about 10 minutes."

"I sure will. Thank you."

That was just what I wanted to hear. I got up and grabbed my bag. I wondered if I should go ahead and change or just wait until we got to the pool? I decided to wait until we got there.

We all had our bags and were waiting by the door. We heard Mrs. Sullivan tell us to come load up the bus, so we did just that. I was third in line to get on the bus. I sat close to the front because I wanted to be one of the first ones off and into the bathroom to change.

We arrived at the pool and we all got off the bus. We had to stand in line while Mrs. Sullivan spoke to the staff at the desk. There were ten of us all together. We stood there talking and laughing, ready to go in. Mrs. Sullivan walked back over toward our group.

"Alright, everyone come over here and make a circle around me so that I can give you all the rules and instructions."

We all listened to her go over everything. She told us how long we were going to be there, what time we would be leaving and what to do if we got hungry. After she finished, the girls went in to the girl's bathroom to change and the boys went into theirs to do the same.

We all came back out one at a time and "walked really fast" to the pool since running wasn't allowed. All you heard back to back to back was "cannonball."

Oh, my goodness gracious! The water was so cold when it first hit my body, but it felt so good on this hot day. Ah, just what I needed. I swam around going lap after lap. After a while, I started doggy paddling over in the area that my friends were in, which was over by the diving board. We were having ourselves a good ole time.

We watched as everyone lined up to go up and jump off the diving board. I wanted to jump off, but I didn't know if I should or not because one, I was just an okay swimmer and two, I was afraid of heights. It also didn't help that the diving board was right above the 12-feet section of the pool, which was super, duper high.

This one boy made it to the top of the stairs and started yelling.

"Look at me, y'all! I'm about to do some backflips into the pool."

We all looked up and stared at him. The next thing we knew, he took off running, slipped and did a belly flop right into the water. All you heard was everyone gasping and then laughing. He came up and said that he meant to do it. I didn't think that he did, but that was just my opinion.

One by one, the boys and girls jumped into the pool. Some did really well and others, well, not so good. I, on the other hand, was just enjoying my time in the sun and in the water.

Then, I heard the dreaded words.

"Hey Makayla, it's your turn!"

"Wait, my turn for what?"

"Come on and jump! We all have done it. Now it's your turn! Come on!"

"Nah, I'm good! Y'all have at it!"

I heard some of the girls and boys start booing me. Oh no they weren't booing me. Whatever! I didn't have to jump in if I didn't want to. I was good right down where I was.

"Go ahead, Makayla. You can do it!"

I looked back over my shoulder and saw Stacy approaching me. She told me she had just jumped off of the board and it wasn't that bad.

"Oh no, I'm okay Stacy. I can swim, but I'm not the best of the best you know?"

"Makayla, it's really not that bad! All you have to do after you jump in and feel yourself hit the bottom is just kick back up and start swimming. You will be right back at the top. I promise it's not that hard, especially since you already know how to swim."

"I don't know about this y'all. I don't think that I could or should do it."

"You got this Kay. I will go back up there and go right before you so that you will see that you have nothing to worry about!"

"Okay, if you go, then I will go."

We swam over to the side of the pool and climbed up the ladder to get out. Even though it was a short walk over to the diving board, it seemed as if it took forever to get there. We reached the bottom of the stairs and just like she said she would, Stacy went up right before I did.

"Now, watch this Kay. You will see how easy it is!"

Stacy made it to the top, walked to the edge of the diving board, bounced a few times and then jumped off. I watched her splash into the water and a few seconds later, she was back up at the top and swimming to the edge of the pool again. It didn't look bad at all.

I thought to myself, 'You got this Kay!' I walked up the stairs. With each step that I took, it seemed as if it was getting higher and higher. Finally, I made it to the top of the stairs. I reached the top and looked down. Why did I do that? It looked as if I was a mile off of the ground. Nope, not today. I turned to head back down the stairs. I heard my friends yelling.

"Do it, do it, do it, do it, do it! You got this Makayla!"

Stacy yelled, "Makayla, you can do it!"

I turned back around and decided to face my fears and jump off the diving board. '*One, two, three!*' I counted to myself. Nope I was still at the top. '*Okay, okay, okay. For real this time,*' I said to myself. I walked to the edge of the board, bounced a few times like I had seen Stacy do and jumped! As soon as I jumped, I immediately wanted to be back on the board going back down the stairs. What was I thinking? Why did I let them talk me into this? It was too late by then. SPLASH! I hit the water!

Now you see, here was the turning point of my day. Everyone before me made it seem so easy, that I was just going to go down, hit the bottom, and come right back up. That didn't happen for me. I knew I should have stayed my tail where I was, and that was in the pool.

Once I hit the water, it felt as if I went down but I never felt the bottom. I started kicking and kicking but I never felt the bottom, nor did I make it back to the top. I immediately started panicking. I was kicking and trying my best to make it to the top. I started to feel as if I couldn't breathe. I tried to hold my breath as long as I could, but it was starting to get hard to do. I kept trying to make my way to the top. I wondered if anyone had seen me or what everyone was doing while I was down there about to die.

I finally made it to the top, but I still wasn't able to get out. It seemed as if every time my head was out of the water, it went right back under. By that time, I was gasping for air. I just knew that I was about to drown.

"HELP!" I screamed out before I went back under.

Whelp, this was it! I was about to die! I couldn't breathe. I felt myself sinking further and further into the pool.

Then, I felt someone grab me and pull me to the top. I gasped for air when I finally had my head out of the water. I was coughing and trying to catch my breath as they pulled me over to the side and then out of the pool.

I couldn't stop coughing. Between the coughing and gasping for air, I started crying. I couldn't believe that I almost drowned.

"It's okay, Makayla! You are alright! Slow, deep breaths!"

I didn't even know who it was talking to me. I just held on tight to them and cried. I heard more and more voices asking if I was okay? "I thought that she could swim!" "Why would she jump in if she couldn't swim?" "That's stupid." I opened my eyes to see that Mr. Davis had been the one to pull me out of the pool.

"Thank you, Mr. Davis!"

"It's no problem Makayla, but why did you jump into 12 feet if you can't swim?"

"I don't know! I can swim but I'm not a strong swimmer. Everyone told me that it was easy and that I would feel the bottom and go right back to the top. But, I didn't feel it. I'm sorry. I thought that it was going to be easy."

"It's okay, Makayla, as long as you are okay and know not to do that again!"

"I will definitely not be doing that again! I just want to go home!"

"Come on. Let's go over to the other side of the pool away from this crowd. That way you can have a minute to get yourself together, okay?"

"Okay!"

Mr. Davis helped me up off of the ground and walked me over to the other side of the pool. We sat on the edge for a while so that I could calm down and get myself together. As he sat there talking to me, I just kept thinking to myself, *'Man, I just can't believe that I almost drowned.'*

We reached the other side of the pool and I saw Mrs. Sullivan coming.

"Makayla. Oh, my God! Are you okay? They told me what happened!"

"Yes, I'm okay Mrs. Sullivan. It just scared me like really bad!"

"I am so sorry, Makayla. I'm going to call your mother and see if she can come and get you."

"It's okay, Mrs. Sullivan. You don't have to call her. I am and will be okay."

"Are you sure, Makayla?"

"Yes, I'm sure. I don't want to have to cut the trip short on something that I did that I shouldn't have done. I am just going to sit over here for a minute, if that's okay?"

Mr. Davis said, "I'll sit over here with her to make sure that she is okay. When she is ready, I'll walk her back over to where everyone is."

"Makayla, are you sure that you are going to be okay?

"Yes, I will be. Thank you for not being mad at me."

"Why would I be mad at you? I just want to make sure that you are okay!"

She leaned in to give me a hug. I closed my eyes and imagined that it was Mommy hugging me. I knew that if Mrs. Sullivan called my mom to tell her what happened that I would get fussed at. Mommy always told me not to listen to other people, especially if I felt that it was wrong. I didn't want to get fussed at today.

"Thank you, Mrs. Sullivan!"

"You're welcome, Makayla! I will be right over here if you need anything okay!"

"Thank you, again!

She walked back over to where she was sitting. It wasn't close, but it wasn't too far away from us either. I stared at her for a while and then at everyone else that was on the other side of the pool. I felt really stupid. I didn't even know why I had gone and jumped off of the diving board. The more I thought about it, the more I started to get upset with myself.

I snapped out of my thoughts though, when I felt Mr. Davis' hand on my knee.

"Makayla, are you okay?"

I must have been staring off in space because he had this concerned look on his face.

"Oh yeah, sorry. Yes, I'm okay. Just still thinking about what just happened, you know?"

"Yes, I know Makayla. I know that you must have been scared to death."

"Literally," I said as I interrupted him.

"I know you were, but you are doing okay now. Do you think that you may want to get back in the water? If you don't get back in you will develop a fear of it because you will only think about what happened the last time you went swimming."

"You're right, but maybe in a few minutes."

We sat and talked for a few more minutes. I felt a lot better after sitting there talking with my feet in the pool. I thought about getting all the way back in the pool, but I was nervous. *'Would I drown for real? Would I start crying? How would it be?'* I figured that I should go ahead and get back in to see how I would feel. So, I did.

"Mr. Davis, I think that I'm ready to get back in."

"That's good to hear. I thought that you weren't going to get back in."

I honestly didn't think that I would get back in either. I still didn't know if I wanted to get in or not, but decided to go ahead and get in. I slid down the side of the pool into the water. Just like the first time, it was cool but calming. I stood right by the edge moving my arms back and forth. I splashed some water on my shoulders. Okay, not too bad. I splashed water in my face. Okay, still not too bad. Here came the true test, to put my head under water.

I took a deep breath and went under. As soon as my head was fully under, I immediately came back up in a panic. When my head was out of the water, I found myself gasping for air again. Mr. Davis came over and put his hand on my shoulder.

"Makayla, are you okay?"

"Yes, Mr. Davis, just got scared for a moment! I'm going to try it again."

"Okay, just take your time and take a couple of deep breaths. You got this."

He stepped back and I took a couple of deep breaths. Here we go again. I slowly put my head in the water. That time wasn't too bad. I held my head under water for a few seconds and looked around. I came back up and that time, I was okay. I was so proud of myself. I did it.

I guessed I must have looked extremely happy or excited because Mr. Davis came over and gave me a hug.

"Great job, Makayla. I am so proud of you for getting back in the water. You just don't know how much you have helped yourself by doing that."

"Thank you, Mr. Davis. I feel a lot better now. I think I'm ready to go back over with my friends now."

"Are you sure?"

"Yes, I am sure and thanks so much for sitting over here with me."

"No problem at all."

Although Mr. Davis had said, "No problem," he still had his arm around my shoulder. I was trying to ease my way from under his arm, but he was just standing there. Then, out of nowhere, he leaned down and kissed me on my forehead.

"Hey, um, so, can we go ahead and go back over with everyone else?"

He tried to lean down and kiss me on my lips.

"Whoa! What are you doing, Mr. Davis? That is so not cool!"

I pushed him away from me so that I could go back over to the other side, but he grabbed me by the waist and told me that I wasn't going anywhere.

"Makayla, why are you playing these games with me? We were over here laughing and talking. You were just flirting with me and now you don't want me to touch you? It doesn't work like that!"

"Huh? What are you talking about? I was not flirting with you! Yes, we were over here talking but I thought it was because I almost drowned. You were trying to calm me down and make sure that I was okay? If that means that I was flirting with you, then I'm sorry because I sure was not trying to!"

"You didn't mean to? Are you kidding me, little girl? Nah, it doesn't work that way! We are going to stay right over here until I say that we are ready to go back over to the other side!"

Now at that point, I was standing in the pool confused as I don't know what. How could he say that I was flirting with him? We were sitting there talking, he kept asking me if I was okay, if I needed anything, if I wanted to get back in the water, but never once did I touch him nor say that I liked him. That's gross.

Even though he was older than us, but not as old as the other people in the office, you could say that he would be considered like the cool dad or cool uncle of the office. He was fun to be around because he made us laugh and always made sure that everyone was okay, but that was it. I did not look at him in any other way, so I had no idea what he was talking about. I just wanted to get away from him as fast as I could because this was quickly becoming awkward. I definitely didn't want anything bad to happen to me again.

"Mr. Davis, can you please let me go? I have already apologized to you. I honestly did not mean to make it seem as if I was flirting with you. I was not trying to. Please let me go! You are making me uncomfortable and I am about to start screaming."

"Oh, you are going to start screaming now Makayla? If you do, I promise you, I will be at your house tonight to kill you. I may even just kill your whole family just for the heck of it. You are going to learn today not to play with a grown man.

I could not believe what I had just heard, again. I wasn't too sure why he had all of a sudden flipped and gotten so upset. Thoughts were racing through my mind. '*I was not playing with him or any other grown man. Why did he think that I was? I can't go through this again! I almost drowned earlier and now he was threatening to kill me and for what? Why, God? Why me? Why do you hate me so much? What am I doing so wrong? I'm only a child! Do all children go through this? What am I going to do now?*'

Mrs. Sullivan wasn't too far from us, but she wasn't super close either. I wanted to scream and get her attention, but would he really kill my family and me if I did? Why do they always say that? This has been such a horrible day. I was looking so forward to coming to the pool and having fun with my friends, and now this.

Before I could even say anything else, Mr. Davis had made his way behind me and was trying to put his hand down in my bathing suit. All I could think was '*Why, just why?*'

I tensed up and as soon as I got ready to scream, Mr. Davis leaned in and whispered in my ear.

"Try it and you will die right now!"

I couldn't do anything but start crying. I didn't want to die. I didn't want my family to die either. I was just hoping that someone would see us and come save me. Mr. Davis had backed us up against the wall and was now in a seated position. He had me pretty much sitting on his lap. One of his arms was still around my waist and the other hand he had down in between my legs.

I felt as he shoved his fingers inside my private part. I had immediately felt a burning and stinging sensation. It was hurting badly. I wanted to replace my tears with screams, but he was still whispering threats in my ears.

"I'm sick of y'all little girls playing us men like we are just going to put up with it. This is what you get! If you make a noise, I will snap your neck right here and now! I will go to your house tonight and kill everyone! Try me if you think I am playing! You are about to see what a real man feels like today since you think you are grown!"

I was scared to try and fight him off. I was scared to say anything or scream out. I was hoping that Mrs. Sullivan or someone would notice what was going on and come get him away from me. The tears continued to fall down my face as he shoved his fingers in and out of me.

"You like this, don't you girl?"

"No, I do not like it at all!" I cried.

"You know you like it, so you better tell me that you like it before

I beat the mess out of you!"

I didn't want to say anything but wondered if I told him what he wanted to hear, would he stop? I did not want to get beat up. I didn't want anything to do with this man. I just wanted his fingers out of me and for him to let me go!

The tears kept falling. I was so sad, hurt and just over it. I decided that I wasn't going to tell him what he wanted to hear. I hoped that if I didn't, he would raise his voice and that someone would hear him and come running over.

All of a sudden, I felt a pain and stinging sensation in my shoulder. I looked over and Mr. Davis had bitten me and was still clamped down on my shoulder. I didn't mean to but I hollered out from the pain.

"Owwwww!" I cried.

"Shut up right now, Makayla!"

"Please let me go, Mr. Davis! Please! I promise I won't say anything! I won't tell anyone! Please, just let me go!"

"You're dead!"

I cried for him to let me go, but he was still holding onto me. I looked up and happened to see that Mrs. Sullivan and a few other people had gotten up and were starting to walk over toward us. Thank you, God! She was coming to save me.

Mr. Davis quickly moved his hand and pushed me forward off of his lap. I was so happy to be getting away from this evil man. I couldn't believe all of the events that happened today. I almost drowned, I was molested, bitten and threatened. All of those feelings were quickly being replaced with the feeling of relief as I saw Mrs. Sullivan getting closer to us.

Finally, they were standing in front of me, but the look on her face had me a little confused. She was looking at me with sheer disgust and disappointment. Maybe she was looking at Mr. Davis. I didn't know, but I was just glad that she was there.

"MAKAYLA! What are you over here doing to Mr. Davis? Get your little fast tail away from this man right now!"

"Huh, wait! I'm not doing anything! He pulled me over here and onto his lap. I have been trying to get away from him for a while now! He wouldn't let me go! I didn't do anything!"

She turned to Mr. Davis and asked, "What is she doing to you?"

"Mrs. Sullivan, she was trying to get me to have sex with her in the pool! She said that she wanted to pay me back for being so nice to her and for calming her down. I kept telling her "no" but she came and sat on my lap. She told me that if I made any noise, she would say that I was trying to rape her! I'm sorry. I know this looks very inappropriate, but I was trying to get her to understand that she doesn't have to use her body for payment and especially not at this age!"

"Wait! Why are you lying? I did not say anything like that and you know it! You told me that if I said anything or made a sound that you would kill my family and me! Tell the truth!"

"Makayla! You know that I said no such thing! I kept trying to tell you that we needed to go back to the other side where everyone else was, but you said that you didn't want to go. You even put your head under water saying that you wanted to have oral sex with me first. I told you that it was very inappropriate the way that you were acting!"

"Why are you lying, Mr. Davis? You know good and darn well that it did not happen like that! What about the bite mark on my shoulder then? How do you explain that?"

"Makayla, that is not a bite mark! When I was trying to push you up off of me, you threw yourself back into me and your shoulder hit me in the mouth."

"Are you freaking kidding me right now?"

"Makayla, get out of the pool right now!"

I couldn't believe what was happening. He literally just stood in all of our faces and lied. How could he just lie like that? I could not believe it. How could Mrs. Sullivan believe him over me and why would she even think that I was trying to do something to or with him? It just didn't make sense at all.

I had never been accused of anything like that before. I didn't know what hurt more, him shoving his fingers in and out of me or her accusing me of trying to do something with that man. Either way, I felt horrible and was over the whole day. I just wanted to go home and cry.

I made my way over to the stairs and then out of the pool. I was hoping that she would know that he was lying and that I was telling the truth. I was hoping that she would see that I was hurting and scared. I thought to myself, *'She couldn't possibly believe him. I just knew that once we got away from him that she would ask me what was wrong. Maybe she would even call the cops on him after calling my parents. She had to see that I was telling her the truth. She just had too!'*

"Makayla, what in the world were you thinking about? Why would you be over here trying to have sex and oral sex with this man? What is wrong with you?"

"Mrs. Sullivan, I swear that I wasn't trying to do anything to or with him. He was trying to force me to have sex with him, not the other way around. I wouldn't do that. Please, you have to believe me. I am telling the truth."

"Why would he lie on you? He is a grown man with a family and a good job! He doesn't need to mess with you and risk it all. See I knew it was something about you. You are fast, hot in the pants and out here acting like a whore like you do not have any home training. You ought to be ashamed of yourself! What would your Mother think?"

Wow! Just wow! How could she even say that to me? I'm just a child! I didn't do anything wrong. I couldn't figure this out. She had already made up her mind that I was lying without even seeing what happened or hearing my side of the story. For her to say that I was "out here acting like a whore" was uncalled for. My feelings were so hurt.

"Are you serious, Mrs. Sullivan? 'Out here acting like a whore with no home training?' Are you kidding me? Well obviously, you have your mind made up! There is really no point in talking about this anymore, especially since you want to call names! Can you just call my mommy and have her come pick me up?"

At that point, I was over her, the conversation, the near drowning, the molestation, him lying on me and her accusing me. I just wanted to go home, shower and lay in my bed. I didn't understand why these things kept happening to me.

"Yes, I am serious Makayla! Yes, we are about to leave now. This definitely cannot and will not be tolerated! Go and get your things NOW!"

"Whatever!"

I stormed off and went to get my things together. I had so many things racing through my mind. *This could not be happening! What would Mommy and Daddy say? Will they do and say the same things that Mrs. Sullivan said? Should I even try and explain what happened? I should just keep my mouth closed. Mrs. Sullivan already doesn't believe me and thinks that I act like a whore,* why would anyone else believe me?'

I grabbed my things and went into the bathroom. I stood in the stall and cried. I hated Mr. Davis for what he did to me, but I hated him even more for lying on me. I heard Mrs. Sullivan yelling.

"Let's go, Makayla!"

I walked out of the bathroom and headed towards the bus. I stood in line as we each got on one by one. I was so emotional and aggravated. I stepped onto the bus. As soon as my foot hit the step, I heard Mrs. Sullivan calling my name.

"Makayla, you sit right there on the second seat!"

"Why do I have to sit up front, Mrs. Sullivan?"

"Because we are not about to have any more incidents with you today. Now sit down like I told you to."

I wanted to go off on her so bad. She was so wrong for the way that she was treating me. I didn't do anything to her or anyone else. But, what could I say? She had already made her mind up about me. At that point, I had given up. I just didn't care anymore.

I got on the bus and sat in the second seat. I turned, looked over my shoulder and saw that everyone else had gotten to sit where they wanted to and with their friends. Not me though. Because of that monster, I was stuck in the front of the bus.

Mrs. Sullivan, Mr. Davis and a few other people were standing outside of the bus by the door. I could hear that they were talking about me and what they thought that I had done. The more they talked, the worse I felt. I wondered if they knew how they made me feel. It probably didn't even matter to them.

Finally, they all got on the bus. Mr. Sullivan and a few other ladies sat in the first two seats. Mr. Davis got on and walked past me. As he was walking by he said, "You're dead!" He didn't say it out loud, but I knew what he said.

I sat there in my seat with tears falling down my face. Did he really just threaten me again? I'm dead? Why? Because I wouldn't go along with his lies? Fine, I didn't even care anymore. If he was going to kill me, then so be it. It didn't matter. No one would believe me anyway. I sat there the entire bus ride back to the office just thinking about how everything went down. I was interrupted when I heard Mrs. Sullivan say my name.

"I don't know who Makayla thinks she is. Giving me attitude because she is a whore! I can't stand these ugly, fast-acting little girls. You know the apple doesn't fall far from the tree. She probably is just doing what she sees her mother do. Out here whoring around with no respect for herself and at such a young age!"

I was so angry! She had really gone overboard with her statements. Really? And she was supposed to be an adult. I sure couldn't tell. In my mind, I had already gone off on her and tried to fight her. But I didn't say anything. I didn't utter one word. I just sat there, listened and cried.

We made it back to the office. I ran off of the bus and straight to the car. I was so glad to see Mommy, but I didn't and couldn't even tell her what happened that day.

"Hey Makayla! How was your day today? Did you have fun today? Why am I even asking you that question? I already know you had a blast!"

"Yes Mommy, today was okay. I am just tired. Can we go home please?"

"What's wrong with you? Everything okay?"

"Yes Mommy. I'm okay, just really tired from being out in the sun all day."

"Oh okay. Yeah you look tired. Your eyes are super red. That chlorine must have aggravated your eyes. It's okay. When you get home, you can take your shower and go to bed. We will talk about everything tomorrow, okay?"

The ride home was a silent one. I pretended I was asleep so that I wouldn't have to talk about the day. When we pulled into the driveway, I sat up and took off my seat belt. I grabbed my bag and got out of the car. I was heading inside when I heard Mommy talking to me.

"Huh? What did you say Mommy?"

"I was just asking if you were sure that you are okay? It seems as if something is bothering you."

"I'm okay. I'm just really tired."

She walked around to where I was standing and gave me a hug. I wanted so badly in that moment to break down and tell her what happened today, but what was the point? Who would ever believe this little ugly, whore acting, no-home-training little girl? I didn't even think that my own mother would believe me.

I just wanted to go inside, take a shower and go to bed. I didn't think that I could take anything else that night.

"Thank you for the hug, Mommy. I'm about to go in and take my shower, okay."

"Okay Makayla. Sleep well and I will see you in the morning."

"Okay Mommy!"

I walked in the house and went straight into the bathroom. I turned on the water, sat down on the toilet and cried. I couldn't stop the tears from falling. I made sure to keep silent while I was crying because I didn't want anyone to ask me any questions.

I was so angry and hurt. I wanted to literally claw myself out of my own skin. If I could, I would have. I looked in the mirror before getting in the shower and thought, *I hate you with your ugly self! You are ugly and a whore! No one will ever like you!'*

I turned away in disgust and got in the shower. I cried the entire time that I was in there. I just couldn't believe what happened to me that day. Everything was my fault. And no one even cared that I almost drowned!

Hey Sis, Can You Do My Hair?

Ring, ring!

Ring, ring!

Ring, ring!

"Hello?"

"Hey, can I speak to Makayla?"

"Speaking."

"Hey Kay, what you up to today?"

"Who is this?"

"Stop playing. You know who this is, girl!"

"Umm, no I don't. Who is this?"

"It's Ryan. Quit playing, Sis!"

"Oh hey, what's up, Ryan? My bad. I didn't recognize your voice. Nothing much. What's up with you?"

"Nothing much. I was calling to see if you could come do my hair today before the game? Maybe in like an hour or so?"

"For sure. No wait. Hold on a second. Let me ask Mommy. You know how she is, lol."

I lowered the phone from my ear and called out for my mom. I knew she hated when we hollered for her instead of just coming to her.

"Mommy!"

"Mommy!"

"Ryan, let me call you right back. I have to make sure that it is okay with Mommy, but I don't see her at the moment."

"Ok cool. Call me back and let me know what she says, okay Sis?"

"Okay, I sure will."

As I hung up the phone, I thought to myself, '*Where is Mommy and why isn't she answering?*' She was probably just ignoring me. She always said that if we want anything to come and ask her. Don't be doing all of that hollering. I still called out for her just to see if she would answer, though. I knew she was probably just sitting in the kitchen.

I walked out of my room and went into the kitchen. Nope, she was not in the kitchen. I peeped my head in the living room. She was not in there either. Hmmm, I hope she didn't leave and not tell anyone.

"Mommy!"

"Mommy!"

"Maaaaa, where are you?"

I went to her room and knocked on the door.

"Makayla, girl why are you hollering? Haven't I told you about that before? Just come out of your room and get me instead of doing all that yelling!"

"Sorry Mommy, but I called out for you about three times already. I thought you had left."

"Child, no. I'm in here cleaning up. But if you would have come out of your room, then you would have known that I was in here. What's wrong with you?"

Now at that point, I wanted to get smart right back with her by saying, *'Well if you would have just answered me when I called your name then you would have known that I wanted something.'* That would never come out of my mouth, especially not to Mommy. She was crazy. And I definitely didn't have time to be losing any teeth over having a smart mouth.

I could have sworn that she had eyes and ears in the back of her head and all over our house. If we even tried to mumble something under our breath, she would be like, "Excuse me, did you have something to say?" We could be all the way on the other side of the house and she would still hear us. Nope, not today. I'm not trying to get smacked in my mouth and put on punishment.

"Oh, nothing, Mommy. Ryan just called and asked me if I would come do his hair today before the game tonight. Would that be okay?"

"Yes Makayla, that's okay but before you go up there, make sure that your room is cleaned and that those dishes are washed and put away, okay?"

"Okay, I will go do it right now."

"Okay and you know to be back in this house before it gets dark outside, right?"

"Yes, I will be back home way before it gets dark Mommy."

"Okay, tell Ryan and his grandmother that I said, 'hello.'"

"I sure will Mommy."

"Ring, ring"

"Ring, ring"

"Hello?"

"Hey Ryan?"

"Hey Kay!"

"I just asked Mommy and she said that I could come over in a little bit to do your hair. So, I will be up there when I get finished cleaning, okay?"

"Okay cool, Sis. I will see you in a little bit!"

"Okay, oh and she told me to tell you and your grandma "hello.""

"Okay cool Sis. Tell her that we said, 'hello' also."

I hung up the phone and walked to my room. I thought to myself again, *How come every time I ask to do something or go anywhere, she always tells me to go clean up. Like why can't I ever just do what I want to do or go where I want to go without having to do something first?*

You know what though, I'm not even going to say anything or complain today. I'm just going to go ahead and do it. Besides, it wouldn't do anything anyway. Knowing her, she probably already heard my thoughts. Mommy would have definitely changed her mind quick, fast and in a hurry if she heard me mumbling. She didn't play at all.

I got back to my room and looked around. Man, my room was not even that dirty, just a few things here and there. I wondered if I pushed my clothes into my closet would she even notice. Nah, I better not do that. It would be just my luck that the day I decided to do that she would go and look in the closet. Let me stop this complaining and get this room cleaned up. Although it took a little longer than expected, I finished cleaning my room.

After my room was cleaned, I hopped in the shower. I had worked up a sweat while I was cleaning up. I got out and dried off. I threw on some shorts, t-shirt and shoes. I walked back to Mommy's room to let her know that I was about to leave.

Knock, knock!

Knock, knock!

"Hey Mommy. I'm finished cleaning up. I'm about to head to Ryan's house and I will be back in just a little bit, okay?"

"Okay, Makayla. Make sure that you are back home before it gets dark!"

"Okay, Mommy!"

I grabbed my keys and walked out of the door. Man, it was hot outside that day. If I have known that it was so hot, big bro definitely would have been coming to me to get his hair done. Whew! There was no wind blowing or anything.

I was so glad that Ryan didn't stay too far from us because I was so tempted to go back to my house to call and tell him to come down to our house.

"Hey Kay!"

Startled, I turned around and it was Jocelyn running up behind me.

"Hey girlie, what are you doing out here today?"

"Nothing much. Just came from Granny's house about to go home. Where you going, Kay?"

"Girl, about to go up to Ryan's house. He called me a little earlier and asked if I could do his hair before the game tonight. You want to come with me?

"Girl no. It's too hot to be out here walking. I'm going right over here to my grandma's house where it's cool. I will go with you next time, though."

"Okay Jocelyn. See you later, girl!"

"See you later, Kay!"

She was right. It was too hot to be out walking. I was glad that I was almost there. Ryan's house was the next street over from where I was.

Whew, I finally made it! I walked into their yard and onto their porch. The steps made a funny noise as I stepped on each one, as if it was going to collapse. I looked down at each step until I got to the top of the stairs.

Knock, knock!

Knock, knock!

"Who is it?"

"It's Makayla!"

"Hey, Sis. Come on in," Ryan said as he opened the door for me.

I walked in behind Ryan. The door made this loud squeaking sound as it closed behind us. It kind of scared me and made me jump. I hadn't heard an old house noise like that since I was at my grandparents.'

"Dang, Ryan. Y'alls house is old, lol. Does it make noises like that all the time?"

"Girl, now you know my grandma has had this house forever. So, don't be up here talking junk about it."

"Yeah, yeah, yeah whatever. I'm just saying. First, I thought that the stairs were going to collapse under me and that door just almost gave me a heart attack. Y'all need to put some oil on it or something," I said jokingly.

"Ha, ha, ha, Sis. You got jokes today, huh?"

"You know I'm right. Anyways, do you have the comb and brush already?"

"Yeah, it's right over there. Let me grab them."

"Oh, and can I get something to drink while you are over there too, please?

"Yeah, hang on. Let me go grab you something. You want soda, juice or water?"

"I'll take some soda please and thank you!"

While Ryan grabbed the comb, brush and something to drink for me, I walked over to the couch and sat down. He came back in the room and handed me the comb and brush. He sat the drink down on the end table beside us and sat down in front of me. I started doing his hair.

"You want to watch TV or listen to music while you do my hair, Kay?"

"We can watch TV. That's fine."

He turned on the TV and started flipping through the channels. He stopped on *Martin*. Man, I absolutely loved that show. I thought it was the best TV show ever. We were sitting there laughing and cracking ourselves up as we were copying what the characters were doing.

Out of nowhere, I started tapping my foot. Man, I had to use the bathroom like really bad. I knew I shouldn't have had all that dang soda. All that laughing we were doing didn't help me not one bit either. Goodness grief!

"Hey Ryan, do you mind if I use the bathroom? That soda done hit me!"

"Yeah, go ahead Sis. The one in the hallway is not working, so you will have to use the one in my room. It's the second door on the right."

"Ok cool. Thanks! I will be right back."

I hopped up and ran down the hall to Ryan's room to get to the bathroom. I couldn't get in there quick enough. I didn't think that I had that much to drink, but my bladder was screaming otherwise. I finally made it to the bathroom and hovered over the toilet. Whew, what a relief.

I was in the bathroom thinking to myself, *Man this house is old. The floors were making all kinds of noises when I was running down the hall. And who had lace curtains anymore? Wait!!! Was that really a quilt on his bed? Oh my, wait 'til I tell Jocelyn about this.'*

We've hung out at Ryan's house plenty of times before, but I had never been in his room or bathroom. I knew it was old but not this old. It really reminded me of my grandparents' house. Although their house was big and nice, it was still creepy. Every part of the house made a noise.

I finished using the bathroom. I washed and dried my hands, turned off the light and walked out the bathroom. I wanted to hurry up and get finished with Ryan's hair so that I could get home. His house was really giving me the creeps.

I walked out, closed the bathroom door and turned to walk back through the room.

"Ahhh! Ryan, boy! You scared the mess out of me! What's wrong? Why are you just standing right there like that?"

"My bad, Kay! Nothing is wrong. I was just making sure you were good. You were in there for a minute. You okay, Sis? You got the bubble guts or something?"

"Boy! No, I don't have the BG's. But, yeah, I'm good. I was just in there tripping myself out on how old this house really is. I mean, I should have known by them stairs and that front door creaking when I came in."

"Yeah, yeah, yeah. Whatever Makayla! Come on with your funky butt!"

"Okay, my bad. I see you not finding it funny. But my butt is not funky, honey! Anyways, are you ready to get finished? I don't have that much more to go."

"Yeah, I'm ready!"

I could kind of tell that Ryan was not finding it funny that I was making jokes about his house. I mean, I was only joking. Well kind of. The house WAS really old and it DID make noises, but I didn't mean any harm by it though. By that time, I just wanted to finish his hair and go home. It had gotten kind of awkward.

I tried to walk past him so that I could go back to the living room, but he was standing at the foot of the bed. I tried to get around him, but he blocked me so I backed up to see what was going on.

"Um, you okay Ryan? I didn't mean to hurt your feelings! I was only joking."

"It's cool. I'm okay."

"Okay, well can I squeeze by you so that we can get finished?"

I tried to walk past him again, but he was still just standing there not saying anything.

"Um, is there a reason why are you not letting me pass you?"

"Um, Kay?"

"Yes?" I answered with a confused look on my face.

"Did I tell you that you look good today?"

"Huh? No but um thank you! You ready to get finished?" I asked as I was pointing towards the door.

"You're welcome. Yeah, I am but can I ask you something?"

"Sure, what's up?"

"Did I ever tell you that I had a crush on you?"

"Boy! Stop! I look at you like my brother! That's nasty! Come on here and stop playing so that I can finish your hair and go home!"

I tried to push past him, but he held his arm out to stop me from leaving out of the room.

"I'm for real Kay. I know that we have been cool for a while now and that we call each other brother and sister, but I really do like you. For real!"

"So, this is so weird. I'm sorry but I didn't know that you had a crush on me or liked me. I hate to say this but I don't want to be anything more than friends. I hope that you understand. But, let's go ahead and finish your hair so that I can get home. You know that I have to be home before it's dark!"

"You not even going to give me a chance, Makayla?"

"Ryan, no. I'm sorry, I can't!"

"So, you are just going to come up with your little shorts on knowing that I've had a crush on you for a while. You are really telling me that you haven't felt the same way?"

"Ummm, no I haven't felt the same way. I honestly look at you as just a friend, Ryan. Almost like a brother. Nothing more, nothing less! Now can we please go and finish your hair?"

"For real Kay, I'm trying to be with you."

"You know what? I'm just going to go home. This is getting so weird. I will see you later."

By that time, I was agitated. Ryan and I have been friends for a few years now. He came to our house and hung out with my family. He played basketball with my dad and brother at the park. He even called Mommy his mom every time he saw her. Now he wanted to say that he liked me. Nope, I did not want to be more than just friends.

Although he was cute, average height, medium build with great hair, he was not my type. I never even thought about it. I just didn't see him that way, nor did I want to see him that way. He was definitely making me feel uncomfortable. I didn't want our friendship to change, but he seemed as if he was getting upset because I said, "No."

I tried pushing past him again, but this time he grabbed my arm. He had a really tight grip on it, too. When he grabbed me, I immediately got angry!

"Ryan, boy if you don't let my arm go! What is wrong with you?"

"Kay, I know that you want me just as much as I want you. You can't honestly say that you don't. Seriously, why else would you be up here? You know I didn't call you up here just to do my hair right?"

"Uh, yeah. I honestly thought that's why I came up here but since you really don't need it done, I'm about to go home. This is getting too weird! I'll see you later!"

Before I could even push past him, he grabbed me by my hair and dragged me over to the side of the bed. His grip on my hair got tighter and tighter as he was pulling me. He took his other hand and grabbed me by my face. His hand was over my mouth and chin. He threw me back onto the bed and got on top of me.

"Ryan, get off of me! What are you doing?"

"Shut up, Kay! You know you want me! Stop playing these games with me!"

"No, I really don't. I already told you that I didn't! Now get off of me!"

I could not understand how he just snapped like that. I've never seen this side of him before. He was always so laidback, except for when we were cutting up and having a good time. We had literally just been sitting in the front room laughing and talking while I was doing his hair, and now this. I couldn't believe this was happening AGAIN!

"Ryan, get off of me NOW!"

My words were useless. He definitely didn't care that I was hollering in his face. I was screaming and kicking, tossing and turning trying to get him off of me. Man, I could not believe what was happening!

"Kay, didn't I tell your ugly butt to shut the heck up? You asked for this so shut the heck up and take it!"

Next thing I knew, Ryan punched me in the side of my face. I could not believe that he had hit me. Not my brother, my friend. The pain that I felt from his hit was unbearable. Why was this happening? He asked me to do his hair and that's all that was going on. Then he just flipped.

I knew that I had been cracking jokes on his house, but I honestly meant no harm. I didn't mean to upset him. And, I honestly didn't know that he liked me. If I had known, I would have told him that I only wanted to be friends. I just couldn't believe this.

I must have blacked out for a moment because after feeling the pain from his hit, I was suddenly gasping for air. Not only had he dragged me by my hair to the bed, jumped on top of me, punched me in my face, but now he was choking me. I was clawing at his arms and face or whatever I could reach. I was trying so hard to get him off of me, but his body weight against mine was way too much for me to handle. I was only 100lbs soak and wet. The more I fought, the tighter his grip got. The tighter his grip got, the more I felt as if I was about to die.

He finally moved his hand from my throat down to my shorts.

"Ryan, PLEASE STOP! This is not you! You do not have to do this! Please just let me go!"

"You must be ready to die today, Makayla! Say something else and that's it! You have been trying to play these little games saying that you don't want me when I know you do! Say one more thing and that will be your last breath!"

The fear and sheer terror that went through my body at that moment! I didn't want to get raped or molested again. Nor did I want to die. I didn't know what to do. We went from laughing in the front room to him raping me in his bedroom and saying that if I made another sound that he was going to kill me. The only thing that I could do was start crying. I tried to keep as quiet as I could, but I was so afraid of dying in that very moment. I just couldn't stop crying.

All of a sudden, I felt a burning sensation going down my inner thigh. I just knew that he had stabbed or cut me. I glanced down as best as I could to see why it was burning so badly. In the midst of him ripping my shorts off, his nail scraped the inside of my thigh. I didn't know if I should have been relieved that he didn't stab me or hopeful that if he was going to kill me that he would just go ahead and get it over with and not torture me to death.

I felt my shorts rip as he snatched them off of me. My panties were off as well. I laid there exposed as I feared death and being taken advantage of again.

Once he had me naked from the waist down, he grabbed both of my arms, crossed them over chest and held me down. Although they were across my chest, they were closer to my neck. So, I felt like I couldn't breathe.

"Open your legs, Kay!"

"No!" I mumbled.

"You must be ready to die, right?"

"Please, don't do this Ryan! I'm begging you!"

I felt another hit but this time it was in my stomach. I yelped out in pain. I couldn't believe that not only was he trying to rape me, but I was getting beat as well. In the midst of everything, I started praying, *'Please God! Please just let him finish or either kill me now!'*

"Open your legs! Now!"

I still didn't open my legs, but he took his knee and pushed it down in between my legs to get them open. And, the pain that I felt from the pinching feeling when he did that. Because my thighs were being pressed into the bed by his knee, it felt as if they were being pinched super hard. That pain alone made me jerk my legs open to get them from under him. When I did, he kneed me right in my private part. I cried out in pain, but he pushed down on my arms, which made it hard to keep crying.

Next, I felt him entering me. I felt as if I was being ripped to pieces. At first, I couldn't tell if he put a broken glass bottle in me or if it was himself. Either way, it was extremely painful. I just wanted it to be over. He pounded my insides. The pain I was feeling down there and in my stomach was becoming so unbearable that I thought I was going to pass out. Then again, I didn't know if I would pass out because of the way he had my hands or from him raping me. I prayed that it would be over soon, but just as that thought entered my mind, he pulled himself out of me and flipped me over.

Now I was laying on my stomach as he entered me from behind. I cried out in pain again. I wasn't trying to, but my screaming in pain was making him go harder and harder. I tried to keep my cries silent, but there was no way that I could. With each stroke, I felt as if I was ripping and burning. I prayed again, 'God, do you hear me? Please God, make him stop. I can't take this pain anymore! Please!'

Finally, I heard him start making these grunting noises and I realized that he had finished. I tried to pull away from him so that he could get out of me, but he grabbed me by my hair and stood me up. He grabbed me by my throat, but all I could do was look down and cry at the sight of all the blood on the bed. I knew that I was in pain, burning and felt as if I were being ripped, but I didn't know that I had actually started bleeding.

"Did you like it?"

Wait! What? He had to be freaking kidding me. Did I like it? Did I like being raped? Did I like being beat? Oh yeah, he was crazy for real. I couldn't even answer. I just stood there in his grasp looking down at the bed while the tears continued to fall down my face.

"It's okay Sis. You don't have to say anything. I already know that you enjoyed it."

He was seriously sick. He really thought that I enjoyed myself? I just wanted to go home. I did not want to look at him anymore, nor did I want to hear his voice. We were definitely not brother and sister anymore nor would we EVER be friends!

"Can I please go home?"

"Hmmm, let me think. It depends! Are you going to tell anyone about this?"

I wanted to say "Yes." I wanted to say that I was going to run home as fast as I could and tell my Daddy what he did to me. I just knew that Daddy would try to kill him for hurting me. I also knew that if I did that, he would more than likely kill me right then and there.

"No, I'm not going to tell anyone! Can I please go home? Please?"

"So, you are not going to tell anyone right?"

"No, I won't tell anyone, Ryan!"

"You know what will happen if you do, right? Well, not just you but your family, right?"

Here we go again! I just didn't understand why every time someone violated me that my family and I had to die if I told anyone. It wasn't bad enough that I was raped and beaten, but to hear that again. I just wanted to go home.

"Yes, you will hurt me and my family, right? Can I go please?"

"Do you think that I would just hurt them? No, I will kill all of y'all! You know all I have to do is sneak in through the back door which will lead me straight into your sister's room right, then to your brother's room, which is connected to yours and your little sister's room. Your parents' room is right next to y'alls room, so it will be easy for me to get to them. If you think that they will hear y'all screaming, don't worry. I will slit everyone's throat so that they can't hear me coming. You got it? So again, are you sure you are not going to say anything?"

What could I say except that I understood? He had literally stood in front of me and told me how he was going to murder my entire family if I told anyone about what he did to me. I was scared out of my mind.

"No, I'm not going to say a word to anyone. May I please go home?"

"Fine, take your lil ugly, butt home. Oh, and you know I didn't have a crush on you right? I just figured I would try being nice before I took it to see if you would have sex with me on your own. Now get out of my face before I change my mind," he said as he started laughing.

I tried to grab and put my shorts back on, but they were ripped. It almost looked as if it was a skirt by the time I had gotten them back on. I didn't care though. I took off running and ran straight out of the house and down the stairs.

The whole way home I was crying and trying to figure out why this had just happened to me. Ryan was someone I considered my friend and brother. Although he wasn't my blood brother, I looked up to him and called him my brother. I trusted him and would have never thought that he could hurt me in that way or in any way for that matter. I was in so much pain. My face was throbbing, my throat was sore, my stomach was hurting badly, too. My private area was aching. I couldn't do anything but cry and continue to run until I got as far from his house as I could without giving out of breath.

I slowed down when I passed Jocelyn's house. I really hoped and prayed that no one was outside, and thank God I didn't see anyone. I tried to catch my breath so that I could get myself together.

I was so afraid. How could I go home and not say anything? How could I even try and sleep during the night knowing that if he even thought I would say anything that he would come in and kill all of us? *'Why me God? Why does this keep happening? When will it ever stop? Is it really because I'm ugly? If so, can I please come be with you so that I don't have to keep going through this for the rest of my life? I can't change the way I look, God. Please help me and make me pretty! Please!'*

I've only been doing hair for a little over a year. Mommy taught me and I have been practicing trying to improve. But today, not only was I violated and beaten while trying to do Ryan's hair, he actually told me how he would kill my family if I said anything. Not to mention that I was called ugly again, too!

I really like doing hair, but I don't ever want to do any guy's hair ever again! Dang, I should have just stayed in the house today. Maybe I shouldn't do hair anymore.

I Should Have Just Gone to School Today!

Ring, ring!

Ring, ring!

Ring, ring!

"Hello?"

"Hey, can I speak to Makayla?"

"This is she. Who is this?"

"Hey girl. It's Robert."

"Oh hey. What's going on Rob?"

"Nothing much girlie. How about you?"

"Same here. What's up?"

"Oh nothing. Just calling to see if you wanted to come hang out with me tomorrow? My mom will be gone all day so we can chill for a minute if you want to."

"Boy, you do know that I have school in the morning, right?"

"Yeah, I know, I know Makayla, but could you come over for a little bit in the morning and then go to school later tomorrow? Please?"

"Boy, are you trying to get me killed? You know Mommy don't play those games."

"Nah Kay, I'm just trying to spend some time with you before I leave. Just for a little while?"

"Okay. Okay fine, I'll be over in the morning before school but not for long though, okay?"

"Okay cool, Makayla. I'll see you in the morning!"

I hung up the phone and thought to myself, now I know good and doggone well that I shouldn't have agreed to go see him, but I did really like him. He was tall, dark and built. He was a star football player at school. All the girls had a crush on him. Every time I saw him outside, he always had on the latest shoes. His clothes were always clean and crisp. He was so cute.

But on the other hand, Mommy was crazy and if she ever found out that I skipped school to go hang out with a boy or skipped school in general, she was going to beat the mess out of me. Decisions, decisions. I mean, what would a couple of hours hurt anyway?

I decided to go for a little bit. This would definitely give me bragging rights. Like little ole me getting to hang out with Robert, the one that all the girls wanted. I just couldn't believe that out of all the girls, he asked me to hang out with him. It would be okay if I didn't go to school just a tad bit late. I'd leave and be at school around 9:30, no later than 10 am! I couldn't stop grinning. I wondered if he knew that I had a crush on him? Oh, my goodness, what if he asked me to be his girlfriend? That would just be amazing! I couldn't even keep this to myself. I had to call and tell Monica.

Ring, ring!

Ring, ring!

"Hello?"

"MMMOOONNNIIICCCAAA!!!"

"WWWHHHAAATTT Girlllll?"

"Guess who just called me? Girl, you are not going to believe it!"

"Who Kay?"

"Nooooo, you have to guess."

"OMG. Girl, if you don't tell me I am going to hang the phone up!"

"Dang Miss Attitude. What's wrong with you?"

"Girl, me and Tyler just got into it over something stupid. Now I'm aggy as I don't know what!"

"Man, I'm so sorry Monica. What happened? You want to talk about it?"

"Okay, so all I did was ask him if the rumor about him and Melissa kissing in the gym over by the bleachers was true. You know what this idiot had the nerve to ask? Who was I going to believe? Him or the little girls that wanted him? It's not like I haven't already heard about him cheating on me before. Girl, he gets on my nerves so freaking bad."

"Moni, no he didn't. Did he really ask you that?"

"Yes Makayla, then he had the nerve to get mad when I told him to just tell me the truth. Matter fact, he didn't even answer my question. He just continued hollering and screaming on the phone. You know what? I'm definitely going to be calling him back when we get off of the phone. But enough about me, girl. Who called you?"

"Dang, now I feel bad for even wanting to talk about my excitement."

"Kay, I'm good. Now tell me who called you."

"Okay, okay, okay! Girlllll, Robert! He called me right before I called you!"

"SHUT UP! You talking about Robert, Robert? As in, ole fine, sexy Robert that used to go to your school?

"Girl YESSSSS!"

"You talking about pretty teeth, smooth waves Robert?"

"YESSSSSSS!"

"You talking about fly, fresh-to-death Robert?"

"Dang Moni, enough with the descriptions! Yes, that's who I am talking about!"

"What did he say? What did he want? Kay you have to tell me everything! How did he sound?"

"He called to see if I wanted to hang out with him."

"MAKAYLA, girl is he going to be your boyfriend? What did you say? When are y'all going to hang out? Tell me. The suspense is killing me girl."

"Monica, how about he asked me to come to his house in the morning and chill with him before I go to school."

"Shut up girl! Are you serious? Are you going? Wait, don't he know that you have to go to school tomorrow?"

"That's the same thing that I asked him, Moni."

"What did he say?"

"He asked me if I would go to school a little late so that I can spend time with him before he leaves."

"Girl, oh he likes you! Like he like you likes you. He wants to spend time with you and get to know you a little bit. Oh, you are his new girlfriend, Girlie!"

Although I was grinning from ear to ear, I still tried to play it off like I wasn't hoping for the same thing.

"I don't know about all that, but it would be oh so cool if he did ask me though."

"What time are you going over in the morning? Girl, you better hope that your mom don't find out! You do know that little lady is crazy right?"

"I know, I know but she will be at work by the time I leave. I think she has to be there at 6am. So, I will have plenty of time. I will get up and get ready early, go hang with him and then go to school."

"Okay girl, all I know is you better call me tomorrow when you get out of school and let me know every single last detail!"

"You already know that I am going to call you, Moni. For now, though, let me get off this phone. I have to finish my homework and clean up. You know Mommy would have a fit if this house is not clean when she gets here."

"I sure do Makayla, but you make sure that you call me tomorrow for real okay?"

"I sure will girl. As soon as I get home."

Man, I promise, I loved my best friend with her crazy self. I wouldn't have traded her for anyone else in the world. We had been friends since the sixth grade. I always called her my proper ghetto friend. She was not from where I was from, so she sounded totally different from me and everyone else. She could also go from 0 to 100 really quickly. But all in all, she was a sweetheart.

The next morning when I woke up, the first thing I did was go straight into Mommy's room to see if she had left yet. Whew, she had already left for work. Perfect! Now I could start getting ready. But before I did, I picked up the phone to call Robert.

Ring, ring!

Ring, ring!

"Hello?"

"Hey, good morning. It's Makayla. Are you up?"

"Hey Kay. Yeah I'm up."

"Okay cool. Do you still want me to come over this morning?"

"Yes, I do. I'm about to hop in the shower, but I will be out and finished by the time you get here. Just knock on the front door and I'll come open it okay?"

"Okay, cool! I'll be there in just a bit!"

I hung the phone up and headed back to my room. I hopped in the shower and started thinking to myself, *'Do I really want to go up here or should I just go on to school? If Mommy ever finds out that I was late to school she would beat me silly.'*

However, I did already tell him that I was coming over for a little bit. You know what, I'm just going to go and pray that Mommy doesn't find out. I got out of the shower, dressed and headed towards the door. Hot dog! I forgot my book bag. I couldn't forget my book bag at home. Mommy would surely have known that I didn't go to school. I grabbed my book bag and headed back towards the door again. Crap, where were my keys? Goodness, I would lose my head if it wasn't attached to my body. *'Think Makayla, think! Where did you put them yesterday?'* I checked my book bag and they were right there in the same pocket. I put my book bag on again, keys in one hand and headed back to the door again. Wait, did I unplug the iron? This time, I let out a big sigh out of aggravation.

I was super-duper nervous and excited, ready to meet Robert but making sure I had everything. I turned around slowly and walked back to my room. I turned the light on and walked over to the iron. Yep it was off and unplugged. *'Okay, Let's try this one more time!'* I mumbled to myself. I made it to the door and off I went!

As I walked up the street, I looked around. Man, it was so pretty outside. The sun was shining but not too much. It was a cool breeze going on but not too hard. There was perfect weather to sit outside on the concourse at lunch. I couldn't believe how pretty it was. Seemed like this may have been too good. Like in a love story, how they set the background when a couple first met. Yes, corny I know, but I almost just wanted to continue on walking to school. But I made it to Rob's house now.

Knock, knock!

Knock, knock!

Knock, knock!

Now I know he didn't have me walking all the way up here and he wasn't even going to answer the door!

Knock, knock!

Knock, knock!

Knock, knock!

See, I knew I should have just walked straight on to school. He had me out here knocking on his door all early and crap.

Knock, knock!

Knock, knock!

Knock, knock!

Ah well! I came up here. No answer! Off to school I'd go. I turned around and started walking back down the stairs.

I heard the door open, so I turned slightly around.

"Aye Kay, where you going girl?"

"I've been out here knocking on the door. I thought you weren't home so I was about to head to school."

"My bad, I was still in the shower. Come on, you can come in."
"Oh okay, I will but only for a few minutes.

I turned and walked back up towards his house. When we got inside, I looked around and thought wow, this was a really nice place! It was so neat and clean. It smelled so good. I couldn't believe that he invited me to his house. I wondered why though. *I mean, did he really like me? Did he want me to be his girlfriend? I really hoped so. I had a crush on him for the longest time. I'm just going to keep my thoughts to myself, though.'*

"Aye Kay, come on Girlie; my room is downstairs."

"Wait, like downstairs in the basement?"

"Yeah, what's wrong? You don't like basements?"

"Nope, not at all. It's just that basements creep me out!"

"Come on. I got you. It was not creepy down here. I promise."

"Ummm!"

He laughed as he said, "Girl come on. I got you. You don't have anything to worry about."

"Okay," I said as I grabbed his hand to walk down the stairs. When we reached the bottom of the stairs, he turned and asked, "See, it's not bad down here, is it?"

"Nah, it's not bad at all. It's actually pretty nice down here."

"See, I told you! You want to watch something on tv?"

"Yeah, that's cool. Hopefully we can find a good show or movie."

Robert went over and grabbed the remote. While he flipped through the channels, I stood over by the door thinking to myself. This was a really nice room. I mean, I imagined that it was nice but this was really nice. He had so many plaques and trophies on his dresser and wall. I knew he was in sports but wow, just wow! Aww, he had all these pictures and medals.

"Makayla!"

"Makayla!"

"Yeah Rob?"

"Why are you still standing over there like you about to run out of the house?"

"My bad. I didn't want to just go and sit down on the bed."

"Girl, if you don't get over here and sit with me and quit acting all shy!"

I sat down on the bed next to him. He had that fresh out of the shower with a light mist of cologne smell. He leaned over, wrapped his arm around me and started talking. Just casual conversation, though, about school, what I liked to do in my free time and what nots. He talked about what he liked to do in his spare time. We were having a really good conversation. I was mainly staring at how white his teeth were though. Man, I hoped that he was going to ask me to be his girlfriend.

"Makayla?"

"Yeah, what's up Rob?"

"You know that I like you right?"

"Honestly, I really couldn't tell. I was hoping that you did because I've had a crush on you for a while now."

"Come on now. You trying to tell me that you never noticed me peeping you out?"

"I really didn't. I hoped that you were but I honestly couldn't tell. You know them girls be all over you so I didn't think I stood a chance."

"Well I do! I'm not thinking about those other girls. I am really feeling you and would like to know if you want to hang out more when I get back? You know, so we can get to know each other?"

I tried not to sound so excited but OMG! On the inside, I was bubbling over with excitement. I couldn't wait to tell Monica. He really liked me.

"Yeah, that's cool with me!"

"I have another question for you, Kay."

"What's up Rob?"

"Can I kiss you?"

"Ummm…"

"If you don't want to, it's cool. I didn't want to do it and you turned away from me, you know?"

"Nah it's okay. Yes, you can kiss me."

He leaned over and placed his lips on mine and we started kissing. It was really nice and gentle. His lips were so soft. I so hoped that I was doing this right.

"Makayla?"

"Yes?"

"Can I lay you back on my bed?"

"Yes, you can!"

He laid me back on his bed. The kissing was so intense, passionate and it felt amazing!

"Wait, wait! Do you have on a condom!"

"It's okay baby. I'm going to pull out. You don't have anything to worry. Trust me!"

"Are you sure about this?"

"Yes, I'm sure! I told you I got you baby!"

We continued on and man was it amazing. And the thought of him calling me "Baby." I was on cloud nine.

He whispered, "I'm about to pull out okay?"

"Yes!" I whispered back.

I never knew that I could feel anything like that. I just laid there thinking, *'Man, when he gets back, I really hope that he asks me to be his girlfriend.'*

I just so happened to glance over at the clock. 10:07am. I knew I should have been at school, but I felt so stuck.

Just in time, well almost. We finished and he asked if I needed to wash up. I told him "yeah." He walked me to the bathroom. He was walking right behind me, arms wrapped around my waist. We were walking, giggling and making small talk. I entered the bathroom and turned on the light. There was a bath cloth and soap on the sink. I washed up and dressed again. Then I walked back into his room.

"Hang on a second Kay, I'm going to go wash up, too. I will be back in a few minutes."

"Ok. NP. I'll wait here for you."

Wow, I felt so special. He really liked me. No one had ever said that they liked me before. Maybe this would actually work. I couldn't believe that we just had sex. I wondered if he wanted to be boyfriend and girlfriend now? Like today! I was not going to pressure him but hopefully he would ask soon. Like when he returned from the bathroom. Or would that be too soon? I meant we did just have sex. I knew it was a little backwards but hey, that would be the next step.

I heard him coming back. Let me get myself together, I thought. I sat up on the bed and the door swung open. I almost passed out. My heart was beating so fast. I didn't know what to do.

"What's up, Makayla?"

"Ummm, hey. What's up DJ? What are you doing here? Where is Rob?"

"Oh, he is coming. He told me that you were here so I was just coming to speak."

"Oh, okay!"

I was sitting there so confused. I didn't even know that anyone else was in the house. I just wanted to run out of his house.

"What's up, Makayla?"

I leaned over and looked passed DJ to see who it was. My palms were sweaty, and my heart was beating even faster now. God, please don't let me pass out.

"Hey, ummm, what's up Tommie? What are you up to?"

"Nothing much, Girlie. I just came down to speak. What you been up to?"

"Nothing at all. Just school, you know how that goes."

"Yeah, I know."

"Hey, what's up Makayla?"

By this time, I stood up. I was feeling more and more uncomfortable by the second. My heart was beating so darn fast. I wondered if they could see it through my shirt.

"Ummm, hey. What's up Cole? How are you?"

"I'm good, Kay. Rob told us that you were down here so we just came to speak."

"Oh, ok cool. Do y'all know where Rob is? I thought he would be finished by now."

"Oh yeah, he will be back in just a few minutes Kay."

I was looking at them and they were looking at me. I was standing up by the end of the bed. They were still standing over by the door. It was almost as if they were in a huddle about something. I just wanted to get out of there. I didn't know where Robert was and I was definitely not comfortable with all of them standing over there.

It was just supposed to be him and me here. A few more minutes passed. I grabbed my book bag and started walking towards the door.

"Well y'all, I don't know where Rob went, but I have to head to school. I'm already way later than I want to be. I will see y'all later. Tell Rob, I waited as long as I could for him to get out of the bathroom, but I have to go now. Okay?"

"Wait Kay, you don't have to leave yet. Rob told us to keep you company until he gets back. He said you would be okay with us."

"Wait, why would I need company if he is just in the bathroom Cole? What do you mean, 'Until he gets back?' So, he left? That's pretty messed up but Nah, I'm good. I have to get to school anyway. I will see y'all later!"

I felt so played. I couldn't believe what they just said. How could he just leave me like that? Why didn't he tell me that he was leaving? I could have left with him and headed to school.

As I tried to walk past them, they all kind of circled around me. That made me even more uncomfortable. I didn't know what they were planning, but I wanted no parts of it.

"Excuse me guys! I need to get through so that I can head to school please!"

"Kay, you not going to leave for real, are you?"

"Yes Tommie, I'm leaving for real! Excuse me."

Cole pushed me back and said, "Girl, you ain't going anywhere. Well at least not until we do the same thing to you that our boy did. Don't worry. Rob said you would be down for it."

"Ummm, wait, what? He said that I was down for what? I didn't tell him anything. He was supposed to go to the bathroom and come right back."

"He told us that you said it was okay for us to you know…"

"I know what, Cole?"

"Have sex with you too, Kay. That's why you skipped school, right?"

"Wait, wait, wait! What? Y'all I did not say that! I didn't even know that y'all were going to be here. He said that it was just going to be me and him here. Please let me go by. I don't know why he told y'all that, but it's so not true."

"Kay stop tripping! He didn't tell you for real? Well we are here now and we trying to hit it, too."

"NOOO! Please get y'alls hands off of me! QUITTT! Please stop smacking my butt! I don't want to do anything with y'all. Robert lied to y'all! Please let me go. Y'all, I'm just trying to go to school."

I had hands all over me coming from every direction. I couldn't tell whose hands were whose. I just started kicking and scratching them. I was hollering, but they didn't care.

"SSSTTTOOOPPP! Y'all are choking me! Listen, I am not having sex with y'all so please stop so that I can go! Stop grabbing me! Get y'alls hands out of my shorts! Pleaseeeeeeeee just let me goooooo! I swear I hate all of y'all. How could y'all even do me like this? Stop trying to kiss me! Get out of my face, PLEASE!"

One of them had their hand around my neck. I almost felt as if I was going to pass out from him squeezing it so hard. One of them had their hand on my breast and it was so painful because he was squeezing so hard. I didn't know which one but one of them had their hand in my panties. I swear I did not want to go through that again.

Here I was thinking that Robert liked me but in reality, he didn't. Why would he do me like this? I started crying, yelling, kicking my feet and swinging my arms. I guess I must have hit one of them because they all stopped and took a step back. I just knew that they were about to beat the mess out of me. I tried to run past them.

DJ grabbed me by my throat, threw me into the wall and said, "Witch, are you freaking crazy? You hit me in my mouth?"

All I could say was, "I'm sorry DJ. I was just trying to leave. I didn't mean to hit you. Can I please just leave?"

"Man, I ought to beat your butt Kay! Go on with your ole ugly tail. Oh, and just FYI, Rob didn't want you. He only asked you to come up here because he knew that you liked him and if he hit it, you would let us hit it, too. But trust, don't nobody want your ole ugly, stupid, cry baby behind. For real though Kay, you may want to get out of here before I beat your butt for hitting me!"

I was shocked. I didn't even know what to do. I just ran out the room crying like what in the world? Why did I even think that he would really like me? All it was, was a set up for him and his homeboys to have sex. I was still in shock and disbelief as I was running up the stairs.

I tripped going up, but I quickly got back up and continued running. I made it to the top of the stairs and ran straight out of the door. I reached the front door, walked out and guess who was sitting on the porch when I made it outside? Rob! Man, you have got to be kidding me! I wondered if he had been sitting there this whole time. I looked him right in the face, rolled my eyes and started walking right back down the stairs. I just couldn't believe it.

Then he had the nerve to ask, "Aye baby. Where are you going? I just came on the porch to smoke. I didn't want you to smell like smoke."

"Rob, don't even try and play me! Your homeboys already filled me in on everything. I'm just a joke to you! You called all of them over here to have sex with me, which was pretty messed up. I skipped school just to come up here and spend time with you. You even told me that you liked me, which was another lie. You never liked me; you just wanted to hit it."

"You know what Makayla, you are right! Girl, don't nobody like your ole ugly tail. I figured you would probably be stupid enough to believe me so hey, why not? And guess what, you were! So, since I was able to hit it, I figured my boys should be able to as well. Did you really think that someone like me could really be into you? Come on now! Seriously? Who would want your ugly behind?""

"Wow, really Rob?"

"Yes, really Kay. Did you hear me stutter? No, you didn't and since you ain't giving it up to them, you can take your little ugly butt on to school now! I got me already and I'm good!"

I stood there in disbelief and regret. I knew it was too good to be true. Why didn't I just go to school? I wouldn't even have gone through this.

"Witch, why the heck are you still standing down there crying? Didn't I tell you to leave?"

Not only did I get my feelings and my heart crushed, but I was insulted and humiliated. To make matters worse as I turned back around to leave, I felt something hit me in the back of the head and then in my back a few more times.

I looked down and what did I see? Rocks! Like really, am I that bad of a person? To make matters worse now they were throwing rocks at me as I was trying to leave. All of them were on the porch calling me all kinds of names and cursing me out.

I couldn't run fast enough. The tears just wouldn't stop falling. My heart was beating even harder right now. I could barely breathe. I slowed down to try and catch my breath when I was on the next street over. Man, how could I not see that he was setting me up? That he really didn't like me? I mean, we talked, hung out and cut up often. But this, man this was so messed up. I couldn't take it. Then to top it all, I got called ugly AGAIN. Not only by Rob, but by all of them.

When would this ever stop? I couldn't even make it to school. I went straight home and showered. I didn't even remember how long I had been in there because I was crying so hard. All I remember was the water getting cold, so I got out and laid across my bed. I buried my face deep in my pillow until it became soaked from my tears. I knew I couldn't stay in the bed long though because Mommy would be home soon.

I got up, went to the bathroom and tried to get myself together. I still looked a hot mess, but oh well. I grabbed my book bag, went out the back door and sat on the porch. Just thinking about the should haves, could haves and would haves. I was still in disbelief. One, that he really didn't like me. Two, that they all really played me. Three, I didn't even make it to school. Man, oh man, I just couldn't believe how my day went. I just sat there staring off in space until about 4 o'clock. When I noticed what time it was, I got up, walked down the stairs and down the path to the next street.

I could have just gone around to the front, but I didn't want it to seem too obvious. I pretty much walked in the shape of a U just to get back to the front of my house. By this time, I was mentally, emotionally and physically drained. I walked up the stairs, put the key in the door, turned the knob and prayed for the best as I walked in.

"Hey Makayla. How was school today?"

"It was good Mommy. How was your day?"

"It was okay! I have a lot of homework to do tonight, though."

"Oh, you do, do you?"

"Yes, I do! I'm going to grab a snack and get started. You need anything before I go to my room?"

"Makayla?"

"Yes mommy?"

"So, you are going to stand there and lie to my face?"

Oh Lord, here we go! Please not today. I just can't handle any more right now.

"Mommy, what are you talking about? I do have a lot of homework tonight."

"Really? Is that the lie that you want to stick to or do you want to tell me the truth, Makayla?"

"I am Mommy. I'm telling you the truth!"

"You are?"

"Yes, I am!"

"Well how come when I came up to the school today to bring you and Sasha some lunch, they said that you were marked absent from school?"

This couldn't have come at a worst time. Of all days, the day that I didn't go to school, she brought us some lunch. I just couldn't catch a break!

"I don't know Mommy but I, I um, I was there today. They must have gotten it wrong in the office!"

"Makayla, you know they wouldn't tell me a lie like that. So where were you and you better tell me the truth?"

I started crying again. I couldn't help it. I couldn't even keep up with the lies. I was so exhausted from everything that went on. I really just wanted Mommy to magically know what happened, take me in her arms and tell me that everything would be okay as I cried myself to sleep. But nope, that wasn't happening.

"I'm sorry Mommy. I shouldn't have lied. I didn't go to school today. I stayed at home because I wasn't feeling well. When I got up and saw that you were gone, I laid back down."

"Really Makayla? So, I've been worried trying to figure out where you were all day when you could have just called my job and had them tell me! Makes no sense at all! You know you getting a whooping right?"

"Mommy, please don't, not right now. I'm really not feeling well. I'm sorry I lied, but please can I get grounded instead?"

"Oh no, you're getting a whooping. You shouldn't have lied. Come on in my room. You know the drill!"

"Mommy!"

"Now Makayla!"

"Ok, Mommy!"

Man, if she only knew what happened to me this morning. I wondered if things would be different. Probably not and I couldn't even bring myself to tell her. I was so embarrassed, so ashamed, so stupid. I couldn't keep going through this. At this point, I didn't even care what happened to me!

"Get up against the wall, Makayla."

"Yes, Mommy," I said softly while trying to hold back the tears.

She grabbed the belt, looped it around her hand and swung. I felt the sting of the first hit and I screamed out in agony. Then the second, third and so on and so forth. I didn't even know if the pain that I felt was from the whooping, getting hit in the back earlier with rocks or if it was a combination of everything that happened. All I remembered was falling to the floor. While the hits continued, she was yelling something but I couldn't even make out what she was saying.

I cried out and pled with her, "Okay Mommy! Please stop! I can't take it anymore! Please Mommy!"

"Well, I hope you learned your lesson about lying to me, Makayla!"

"Yes, Mommy, I did. I'm sorry. It won't happen again!"

I walked to my room and flopped on my bed. I regretted it as soon as my body hit the bed. I was in so much pain. My head and back were already still hurting from earlier and then to get a whipping on top of that.

I thought to myself, *'Can I just die like right now please? Man, I should have just gone to school. This is the worst day ever!'*

Fast forward to 11 weeks later.

Man, I haven't been feeling well at all lately! Seems like I'm always tired. I missed my period but I didn't think that I was pregnant though. He did say that he pulled out so I should be good. Big sigh. Hopefully, I would feel better in a couple of days. If not, I will take a pregnancy test just to be on the safe side.

A few days had gone by, and I still was not feeling well. I went down to the local health department, signed in and sat down. My name was called to go back and take the test. My heart was beating so fast.

"Miss Makayla?"

"Yes ma'am?"

"Please come with me!"

"Yes ma'am!"

We went into this small room and the nurse closed the door behind me. There was a brown paper bag sitting on the counter.

"When was your last period, Miss Makayla?"

"I believe it was May 2."

"Well, you are pregnant! You're almost 12 weeks along."

"Wait! What? I'm pregnant? Oh goodness! Are you sure?"

"Yes Makayla, I am sure!"

"Okay. Thank you," I said. What else could I say at that moment?

The nurse handed me the brown bag filled with vitamins and information. Lord, Mommy was going to kill me! Man, I should have just gone to school that day. I was only 14 and now I was pregnant! He said trust him. Yeah right. I should have known better. Now what was I supposed to do?

Acknowledgements

I would like to first honor and thank God. Thanks goes to my husband Cornellius for always listening, reading, encouraging and motivating me to share my story. To my children who are the loves of my life. Thank you to my family and friends for supporting me, and to Faith Hudgens for bringing my vision for the cover to life!

About the Author

Although known for her Master Braidologist skills, Tameeka Robertson, who was born in Georgia in 1983, has always had a passion for writing, especially poetry. Being a wife, a mother of five and a business owner, her main focus has always been on her family and her business.

At the very tender age of 8, Robertson's traumatic experiences began, which led to her being diagnosed in 2014 with Severe Depression, Panic Attacks, Anxiety, OCD, PTSD, Destructive Thinking and Insomnia. After seeing several counselors, psychiatrists, psychologists and taking eleven pills a day just to be able to get out of bed in the mornings, Robertson decided to seek God to help her heal and resolve problems. Through Him, she reignited her fire and passion for writing.

Through writing, Robertson found that her Healing was within her Healing. Being able to write down her thoughts and feelings, she was able to express herself through words. She prayed and asked God to use her to speak to His people, and that's exactly what He did. She now uses her story to reach other men and women heal from their past. Her motto is "Adjusting Crowns, One King and Queen at a time! Not only is her mission carried out through hair braiding, but through words of encouragement, motivation and inspiration."

Robertson can be contacted for bulk sales, book signings and author appearances at TameekaNRobertson@gmail.com.

If you or someone you know needs any assistance in any of the following areas, please call...

The Childhelp National Child Abuse Hotline - (800) 422-4453

Rape, Sexual Assault, Abuse and Incest National Network Hotline (RAINN) - (800) 656-HOPE

National Domestic Violence Hotline - (800) 799-7233

National Suicide Prevention Lifeline – (800) 273 - TALK (8255)